WATER

KENNETH S. DAVIS, well-known author, was born in Salina, Kansas, in 1912, and reared in Manhattan, Kansas, where his father was a professor of agronomy at Kansas State College. Mr. Davis has been interested in writing since his high school days. Although he majored in chemistry during his first two years at Kansas State, he was very active on the college paper and magazine and eventually switched to journalism. He received his B.S. in 1934, and his M.S. in 1935 from the University of Wisconsin.

Mr. Davis has been an information specialist with the Soil Conservation Service, the editor of a newspaper in an ordnance plant during World War II, an instructor in journalism at New York University, and special assistant to the president of Kansas State. In 1951 he decided to devote all his time to writing. Among his books are: *Soldier of Democracy, A Biography of Dwight Eisenhower* (1945); *River on the Rampage* (1953), an essay on river development; *A Prophet in His Own Country: The Triumphs and Defeats of Adlai E. Stevenson* (1957); and *The Hero: Charles A. Lindbergh and the American Dream* (1959).

As co-author of this book, he writes: "Science, properly presented to the minds of students, *is* a humanizing subject; it's a sad error to set it apart from the humanities and thus deprive our people and our age of that cross-fertilization of aesthetic intuition and exact scientific observation and reasoning which is essential to the building of a world community of human freedom."

JOHN ARTHUR DAY became interested in the various properties of water through his work in meteorology. Born in Salina, Kansas, eight months after Mr. Davis, Mr. Day attended Colorado College, where he received his B.S. degree in physics in 1936. A course in meteorology at the Boeing School of Aeronautics led to a ten-year career as meteorologist with Pan American World Airways.

In 1946 Mr. Day went to Oregon State College after deciding that he wanted to teach and do research. Here he taught physics and meteorology, conducted research in cloud seeding and the behavior of supercooled water droplets, and studied for his M.S. and Ph.D. degrees, which he received in 1953 and 1957, respectively.

A visiting associate professor at the University of Redlands in California from 1956 to 1958, Dr. Day is now an associate professor of physics at Linfield College in McMinnville, Oregon. He is the co-author of *Rudiments of Weather* (Oregon State College Coop Press, 1958) and a contributor to scientific journals. He and Mrs. Day and their children live in McMinnville.

WATER

The Mirror of Science

BY KENNETH S. DAVIS AND JOHN A. DAY

SCIENCE
STUDY
SERIES
○

Published by Anchor Books
Doubleday & Company, Inc.
Garden City, New York

ILLUSTRATIONS BY R. PAUL LARKIN
TYPOGRAPHY BY SUSAN SIEN

Library of Congress Catalog Card Number 61–7644
Copyright © 1961 by Educational Services Incorporated
All Rights Reserved
Printed in the United States of America

THE SCIENCE STUDY SERIES

The Science Study Series offers to students and to the general public the writing of distinguished authors on the most stirring and fundamental topics of physics, from the smallest known particles to the whole universe. Some of the books tell of the role of physics in the world of man, his technology and civilization. Others are biographical in nature, telling the fascinating stories of the great discoverers and their discoveries. All the authors have been selected both for expertness in the fields they discuss and for ability to communicate their special knowledge and their own views in an interesting way. The primary purpose of these books is to provide a survey of physics within the grasp of the young student or the layman. Many of the books, it is hoped, will encourage the reader to make his own investigations of natural phenomena.

These books are published as part of a fresh approach to the teaching and study of physics. At the Massachusetts Institute of Technology during 1956 a group of physicists, high school teachers, journalists, apparatus designers, film producers, and other specialists organized the Physical Science Study Committee, now operating as a part of Educational Services Incorporated, Watertown, Massachusetts. They pooled their knowledge and experience toward the design and creation of aids to the learning of physics. Initially their effort was supported by the National Science Foundation, which has continued to aid the program. The Ford Foundation, the Fund for the Advancement of Education, and the Alfred P. Sloan Foundation have also given support. The Committee is creating a textbook, an extensive film series, a laboratory guide, especially designed apparatus, and a teacher's source book for a new integrated secondary school physics program which is undergoing continuous evaluation with secondary school teachers.

The Series is guided by a Board of Editors consisting of Paul F. Brandwein, the Conservation Foundation and Harcourt, Brace and Company; John H. Durston, Educational Services Incorporated; Francis L. Friedman, Massachusetts Institute of Technology; Samuel A. Goudsmit, Brookhaven National Laboratory; Bruce F. Kingsbury, Educational Services Incorporated; Philippe LeCorbeiller, Harvard University; and Gerard Piel, *Scientific American.*

CONTENTS

INTRODUCTION

Water is an *unusual* substance. At the outset this may seem to you a strange and even absurd statement to make. You have always assumed that "unusual" meant uncommon or rare, and if you refer to your dictionary you will find that this is precisely what it does mean. "Usual," on the other hand, means "such as is in common use" or "such as occurs in common practice." By these definitions, surely, water is about the most usual, the least unusual, substance there is.

Consider it in terms of your daily experience. This morning you bathed in water, brushed your teeth with it, drank it. Perhaps you looked out the window as you awoke and saw water falling as rain, forming puddles and rivulets in yard and street. If you move about much today, the chances are that you will cross a river at least once before evening, or skirt the edge of a lake, and if your home is on one of the Great Lakes or near the ocean shore, you may look out over a seemingly boundless seascape and be reminded that water covers some three fourths of the earth's surface.

Of course, this water is not evenly distributed over the face of the globe. Most of it is held in ocean basins in a state unsuited for drinking or irrigation, being impregnated with salts, while that distilled portion of it precipitated upon the land falls in widely varying amounts from place to place and time to time. Some of you are more acutely conscious of this fact than others are. Those of you who live upon the Great Plains, where burning winds roll up black and terrifying clouds of dust during frequent drought years, or who inhabit man-made oases amidst the deserts of the American Southwest can hardly fail to be more sharply aware of the vital importance of water than are those who live in humid climes. But even you will probably object to our terming "unusual" a substance pervasive of the driest wasteland, as you know better than most. Lakes and streams are buried beneath barren sands. They are parts of a continuous subterranean network, various in form and depth, spread around the world. This system can be tapped with deep wells, and has been, to make water as "usual" for you in the dictionary sense as it is for your compatriots in New England.

Indeed, if water were not "usual" for you in this sense, wherever you may live, you could not live at all. You were literally born of water. For nine prenatal months you swam in it, in the dark warmth of your mother's womb. And if you consider your life as physical process, the whole of it from birth to death may be described with fair accuracy as a flesh-banked and -shoaled stream of water. Every living cell in your body has a fluid interior, a vital solution of various substances in water. Your blood is more than nine tenths water. Your kidneys are sometimes as much as 82 per cent water. Your muscles average 75 per cent water. Your liver is 69 per cent water. Even your bones, your living bones, are 22 per cent water. All in all, you as physical entity are at this moment about 71 per cent water by weight—and this water, evaporating and flowing from the surface of your body, breathed out as vapor on your breath, must be continuously replenished if you are to remain alive. You pour down your throat five times your weight of water every year; by the time you die, if your life span is normal, you will have drunk about 6500 gallons of it.

So intimate is the relationship between water and life that, as Bernard Frank has said, "you could write the story of man's growth in terms of his epic concerns with water."[1] The earliest civilizations of which we have detailed knowledge grew up in flat river valleys of North Africa and the Middle East, where rain is a rare event and surface water hard to find. Probably they flourished there in large part *because* water was scarce: thirsty men must join together in a planned execution of water projects if they are to survive for long in a land of chronic drought. Deep wells must be sunk (Jacob's well of Biblical fame was excavated through 105 feet of rock), canals dug for irrigation (hundreds of miles of them made a garden of arid Mesopotamia a thousand years before Christ), flood waters dammed to insure stable supplies when rivers shrink (five thousand years ago the Egyptians built a rock-fill dam 355 feet long and 40 feet high to hold back Nile floods), and aqueducts raised to transport water over great distances (Solomon ordered the erection of such structures some 950 years before Christ). All these activities require a subordination of individual selfishness to a sense of the general welfare, a harnessing of emotional energies to rational controls, and in general the development of those ethical concepts whereby stable social organizations are maintained. Thus economic specialization

[1] In his essay "Our Need for Water," page 1 of *Water, The Yearbook of Agriculture, 1955*, issued by the United States Department of Agriculture.

and the basic moral tenets of all the great religions may, like you, have been born of water.

But though such considerations convince you that water is an important substance and (in terms of history) an interesting one, they can hardly convince you that it is *unusual*. The latter conviction can come only if you look at water from the viewpoint of the physical scientist. To help you to find this viewpoint and to relate the physical chemistry of water to some of the historic human concerns, is one purpose of this book.

2

But we have also another purpose. We intend to present a general conception of the aims and methods and outlook of science as these are reflected in water and as water is reflected by them. The central subject of this book, in other words, involves not only Water as Physical Fact but also Water as Scientific Idea; and in the development of the latter aspect, our essential theme becomes Science itself—Science as a human activity, an expression of the human spirit, a way of understanding and dealing with the natural world.

By this purpose we shall be led occasionally into realms of theory and history which may seem to you, at first glance, irrelevant to water. They will not seem so, we hope, when you have finished our book. On the contrary, you should by then be reminded once again (for this is precisely the main point we hope to make) that the world, for all its infinite variety, is of a piece and that, in consequence, no part of scientific fact or theory is wholly irrelevant to any other part. Truth is a quality of ideas, not of things, and if there is anything that science has demonstrated with certainty in this dawn of the Atomic Age, it is that every particular truth is an aspect of a continuously evolving Universal Truth: to understand it one must go beyond and beneath it.

Tennyson expressed his appreciation of the interconnectedness of natural phenomena when he wrote a century ago:

> *Flower in the crannied wall,*
> *I pluck you out of the crannies,*
> *I hold you here, root and all, in my hand,*
> *Little flower—but if I could understand*
> *What you are, root and all, and all in all,*
> *I should know what God and man is.*

Every advance of nuclear physics gives further proof of this interconnectedness. It also indicates that the kind of *total* understanding of which Tennyson speaks will never be achieved, since every new truth carries with it implications of the as yet unknown.

There is always a beyond.

CHAPTER 1

The Peculiarities of Water

Some Definitions

Thales of Miletus (640–546 B.C.), the earliest of
the Greek philosophers and men of science, was of
the opinion that the earth was a corrugated disk floating on water inside a star-studded hemisphere which,
in turn, rested upon a boundless expanse of water.
He further believed water to be the original substance
of the universe, out of which everything had been
made[1] and to which everything must ultimately return. ("Water is best" was a cryptic saying of his that
became famous throughout the ancient world.) Aristotle supposed Thales to have arrived at this conclusion from his observation that "the nutriment of
everything is moist, and that . . . the seeds of every-

[1] "The statement . . . ," writes Bertrand Russell in his *A
History of Western Philosophy* (Simon and Schuster, 1945,
page 27), "is to be regarded as a scientific hypothesis and by
no means a foolish one. Twenty years ago the received view
was that everything is made of hydrogen, which is two-thirds
of water." It is now calculated that 93 per cent of all atoms
in the universe are hydrogen and that this element makes up
76 per cent of the universal mass. Helium constitutes 23 per
cent of the mass and well over 6 per cent of the total number
of atoms. This leaves 1 per cent of the mass of the universe
and less than 1 per cent of the total number of atoms to be
distributed among all the other elements: iron, oxygen, mercury, and so on.

thing have a moist nature; . . . and that from which everything is generated is always its first principle." Certainly the theory derived largely from a recognition of the apparent pervasiveness or *usualness* of water.

But we know from Thales's own reported words that he also recognized the *unusualness* of water in its physical properties, for he stressed that water is the only substance that is naturally present on the earth simultaneously and abundantly in three distinct states—the solid, the liquid, the gaseous. On a winter's day it covers a lake as ice, forms the bulk of the lake as liquid, and floats in the sky both as visible cloud and invisible water vapor; boil water, and it becomes steam, invisible at high temperatures or when dispersed in the atmosphere. Undoubtedly these latter observations were as basic to the formulation of Thales's crude cosmology as was his observation of water's apparent universality; without them he could hardly have conceived, as his words imply, the possibility that a block of wood, a breath of air, and a drop of mercury, though presenting themselves to common sense-experience as three totally different things, are made of the same essential stuff.

We now know, of course, that Thales's surmise contained a considerable measure of scientifically demonstrable truth. We know the universe to be truly *one* in its ultimate composition, as the word "universe" indicates, being made up of atoms which, though almost inconceivably tiny themselves, are in turn made up of yet more infinitesimal particles, such as neutrons, protons, neutrinos, and electrons. (When we look at the atom and atomic theory in a later chapter, we shall note that solid matter is, for the most part, empty space!) We also know that all the natural elements occur somewhere in the universe in the same three forms as water does on earth, and can be made to assume any of the three (or most of the elements can) in an earth-bound scientific laboratory. For instance, we say that oxygen is a gas because that is the form in which it occurs in the earth's atmosphere. At a low temperature (−183° C., which is its boiling point), however, it becomes a pale-blue liquid, and at a still lower temperature (−218.4° C.) it freezes into a pale-blue crystalline solid. Similarly we say that iron is a solid because that is the form in which we normally find it on earth. If, however, it is heated to a high temperature (1535° C.), it melts into a liquid which, at 3000° C., boils. Iron, at this point, becomes a gas.

Before we go any further, though, it might be well to define the terms we are using. What do we mean by "solid" and "liquid" and "gas"? At first glance the question may seem foolish, the answers being perfectly obvious; you have known them through your eyes and sense of touch almost from the moment you began to talk. Try to give these answers with the precision required by science, however, or by straight thinking in general, and you are likely to encounter hitherto unsuspected subtleties and difficulties. First of all, you must have it clear in your mind that the terms refer to forms of matter rather than the actual material substance assuming them: whether a solid or a liquid or a gas, iron is iron, water is water, and oxygen is oxygen. In other words, these terms are generalized categories, and each must be defined to include all that is essential while excluding all that is not.

A *solid*, then, has the characteristics of rigidity: it has a definite shape, which is to say that it has a definite boundary and volume, and if it is deformed under outside force, it tends to return to its original shape and size. A *liquid* differs from a solid in that it lacks rigidity or, in other words, after having been

distorted by pressure, it has no tendency to return
to an original shape once the pressure is removed. Indeed, though it has a definite volume, a liquid has no
definite shape; it takes the shape of whatever vessel
contains it. A manifestation of this lack of rigidity is
the fact that, under an imbalance of force, liquids
flow. Some liquids, however, are so viscous (that is,
so slowly or feebly responsive to outer pressures) as
to be hard to distinguish from solids, and it is partly
for this reason that we say that a true solid has a crystalline structure—is made up of crystals, each with a
definite size and shape—whereas a liquid has not.
Glass, by this modified definition, is not a true solid
but an extremely viscous liquid. Lacking crystallinity,
it also lacks absolute rigidity: if you suspend a not too
heavy weight from a glass rod, you will find that the
rod will bend slowly and will not return to its original
shape when the weight is removed. Ice, on the other
hand, is a true solid by this definition in that it has a
crystalline structure and true rigidity. A *gas* is distinguished from both solid and liquid forms in that it
has neither rigidity nor definite volume. Any given
amount of it, regardless of weight or of the number
of atoms and molecules present, assumes precisely
the shape and volume of the vessel containing it,
whatever these may be, since it always fills the vessel.

These three forms or states or phases of matter are
functions of temperature in that they succeed one another, in a given substance, as the temperature of that
substance goes up or down. Any element in a solid
state is frozen. If the temperature is increased to a certain point—a different point for each element—the
element melts into a liquid. If the liquid's temperature is then increased to a certain point, the liquid
boils; beyond that point, the element is in a gaseous
state or phase. The transition between one phase and
another ("phase" being the term physicists prefer) is

not an instantaneous leap: there is a pause, an interval of time during which two phases coexist—a mixture of solid and liquid at the melting-freezing point, of liquid and gas at the boiling-condensation point—while the temperature of the substance remains unchanged by the continued application of heat. Moreover, the temperature at which the transition occurs is directly affected by the atmospheric pressure upon the substance concerned. The higher this pressure, the greater the heat required for a change of phase, though the effect of pressure is much greater upon the boiling-condensation point than it is upon the melting-freezing point. Water, which boils at 212° F. (or 100° C.) under the atmospheric pressure[2] at sea level, boils at progressively lower temperatures as the atmospheric pressure is reduced. Atop a very high mountain, the pressure and, consequently, the boiling point are so low that water is rendered useless for cooking purposes.

Now *heat* is another term requiring in science a much more precise definition than we give it in our daily lives. Of course, each of us through his tactile nerves has the capacity to feel heat and gradations of heat within limits. "We know [therefore] what we mean when we say a thing is hot or cold," writes W. C. Dampier-Whetham in his little book *Matter and Change*,[3] "and we can arrange a series of bodies in order of their hotness, thus getting a first rough scale of temperature. But we soon find inconsistencies in this scale. If we put one hand in hot water and another in cold, and then transfer them both to water which is just warm, we find that this same water feels hot to the hand which has previously been

[2] This is a pressure sufficient to support a column of mercury 76 cm. (about 30 in.) high at 0° C., in a barometer, and is commonly termed one *atmosphere*.

[3] Subtitled *An Introduction to Physical and Chemical Science* (Cambridge University Press, 1924) page 53.

chilled, and cold to the hand which has been heated."
The author goes on to say that a scale inconsistent
with itself is useless for scientific purposes and that
the science of heat could not begin until Galileo, the
great physicist of the Italian Renaissance, made the
first crude thermometer (or, to be precise, thermo-
scope[4]) sometime prior to 1597. Only then could
scientists begin to treat temperature as a truly objective phenomenon that could be objectively measured,
rather than as a subjective bodily sensation.

This, however, was but a beginning. Heat and temperature are not the same thing, though for a century
and a half after Galileo's invention of the thermometer the two concepts were confused with one another, the assumption being that bodies having equal
temperatures "contained" equal amounts of heat.
Joseph Black, a brilliant Scottish chemist and physicist of the mid-eighteenth century, was the first to
make a clear distinction between the two. He treated
heat as if it were a form of matter, an "imponderable
fluid" which was soon named "caloric." Some bodies
were held to have more capacity to absorb this caloric than others; thus he and his followers accounted
for the fact that applications of the same amount of
heat to different substances do not produce the same
temperature changes in those substances. Not until

[4] Galileo's thermometer was a glass tube two or three inches
in diameter with a long stem which was thrust into water and
held there. The bulb was then heated, causing the air in it to
expand, so that some of it was driven down into the stem and
out as bubbles through the water. As the bulb cooled, the air
in it contracted, creating a partial vacuum in the stem. Water
thus was pushed up by atmospheric pressure on the surrounding water surface, and this column of water thereafter rose or
fell with the bulb's temperature, being pushed down by expanding air in the tube or pushed up by outside air pressure.
By calibrating the stem, an observer could take temperature
readings, though very crude ones, which were affected by atmospheric pressure (it varies about 5 per cent daily) and by
the initial temperature at which the calibration was made.

the early nineteenth century was the caloric theory abandoned, and only in the latter half of that century was our present understanding of the nature of heat developed. *Heat*, we now know, is a form of *energy*; the application of heat energy to a substance results in an increased movement, called "thermal agitation," of the molecules of which the substance is composed. The *temperature* of a body or system is, in the words of Linus Pauling,[5] "a measure of the vigor of motion of all the atoms and molecules in the system," or body.

In a solid body these molecules have a fixed relationship to one another. As its temperature goes up, the body's molecules are increasingly energized, vibrating and straining ever more strongly against the bonds of attraction holding them together. These bonds, if one may speak metaphorically, are stretched as a rubber band would be until a sufficient distance has opened between the molecules to cause some of the bonds actually to snap. The fixed molecular arrangement of the solid is then replaced by the random one characteristic of liquids and the still more random one of gases. Thus the freezing and boiling points of a substance are related to its molecular structure; substances of similar structure should freeze or boil at similar temperatures, with the substance having the higher molecular weight (we'll not go into the reasons for this here, but simply state the fact) requiring a higher temperature for change of phase. Knowing the molecular structure and weight of a substance, in other words, should enable one to predict with close accuracy, in relation to similar substances, the temperatures at which the substance freezes and boils.

[5] Page 37 of his *General Chemistry* (Freeman, 1947). Any body is a "system," the latter being a term defined by physicists as "a limited part of the physical world."

Water's Remarkable Heat Relations

Now water, whose chemical formula is H_2O, since each of its molecules consists of two hydrogen atoms combined with one atom of oxygen, is similar in its molecular structure to substances whose formulae are H_2Te (Te for tellurium), H_2Se (Se for selenium), and H_2S (S for sulfur). It would be expected that H_2Te, the heaviest of the four substances, would

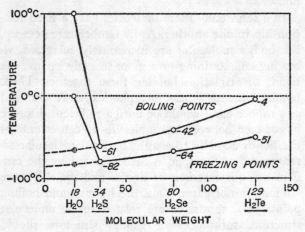

FIG. 1. *The unusualness of water is nowhere better illustrated than in this graph. The upper curve connects the boiling points of water and three other hydrogen compounds of similar molecular structure. The lower curve connects their freezing points. Following the curves from right to left, and noting their smoothness for the tellurium, selenium, and sulfur compounds, you might expect the curves to continue along the broken lines when they come to water, H_2O. Instead, the freezing point of water leaps up from the expected –95 degrees or so to o, and its boiling point from an expected –80 degrees or so to 100 degrees!*

have the highest boiling and freezing points while H_2O, the lightest of the four, would have the lowest. Sure enough, H_2Te, with a molecular weight of 129, boils at $-4°$ C. and freezes at $-51°$ C.; H_2Se, with a weight of 80, boils at $-42°$ C. and freezes at $-64°$ C.; and H_2S, with a weight of 34, boils at $-61°$ C. and freezes at $-82°$ C. But when we come to H_2O, water, which has a molecular weight of 18, an amazing thing happens. On this scale (Fig. 1) it should freeze at about $-100°$ C. and boil at about $-80°$ C., but instead, as we know, the respective points are $0°$ C. and $100°$ C.!

Of course, this peculiarity of water is no violation of the natural order. It can be explained, and we shall endeavor to explain it in a later chapter. But it does indicate that the unusualness of water which Thales stressed 2500 years ago—the fact that it exists in all three phases, solid, liquid, and gaseous, within the range of temperatures and pressures naturally found on earth—becomes increasingly remarkable as we view it through the eyes of a modern physical chemist.

Nor is this the only remarkable thing about water in its heat relations.

Consider, for example, the fact that ice floats. It is an amazing fact when you compare it with the behavior of almost any other substance,[6] and a fact on which life as we know it greatly depends. The general rule, as you well know, is that a substance, whether solid or liquid or gaseous, contracts or shrinks in volume as it is cooled. Nor is water an exception over a wide range of temperature; as its temperature is lowered from $100°$ C., where it condenses from steam, to $4°$ C., it steadily shrinks in volume. But then, all at once, there is a startling reversal of form: instead of further contracting as the temperature is gradually

[6] Bismuth behaves as water does in this respect, but it is one of the very few substances which do.

lowered from 4° toward the freezing point, water gradually expands. It grows less dense in other words, a unit volume of it weighing less at 3° than at 4°, still less at 2°, and so on in steady decline until 0° C. is reached. At that point, the expansion (or decrease in density) is abrupt and drastic (Fig. 2). Water, as it congeals into ice, adds about one eleventh to its liquid volume.

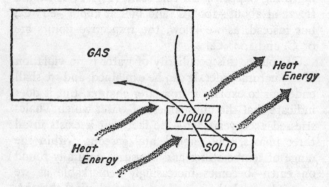

FIG. 2. *Density changes of H_2O as it receives or gives up heat energy are indicated in this diagram. If a unit volume of H_2O in the form of ice occupied the space labeled "solid," it would contract to the size marked "liquid" on receiving sufficient heat energy and then, with more energy, expand to the space labeled "gas" when it vaporized. On losing heat energy, the process would reverse, as indicated by the arrows.*

This expansion can have disastrous effects on the householder's plumbing bill during a season of bitter cold. Water freezing in pipes will burst them, as you may know from costly experience. But on the whole this peculiarity of water is extremely fortunate for mankind and for all life, since, among other things, it prevents a permanent locking up of a large part of the earth's water in a form unavailable to living creatures. Think what would happen if ice were heavier than liquid water. Lakes and streams and seas would freeze from the bottom up as their temperature went below 0° C.; they would become solid blocks of ice, the great bulk of which would remain unmelted during the summer months in temperate climates. And indeed, the whole pattern of climate and weather as we now know it would be sadly deranged. There would be much less evaporation of water and therefore much less precipitation as rain or snow; there would be much more icy weather over the earth's face. The whole moderating effect of liquid water and water vapor on climate and weather would be drastically reduced.

This effect is very great. It can be indicated by reference to the experience of American GIs who served in North Africa, a desert region, during World War II. The Americans, and particularly those whose native homes were near the sea, were as amazed as they were dismayed at a daily fluctuation in temperature unprecedented in their experience. At midday, a sky of brass cast down upon them a withering blast of heat, augmented by reflection from sands hot enough to fry eggs. But at midnight they shivered in a bone-chilling cold. By then the sands were drained of heat and the frigid dark of outer space pressed down remorselessly. Responsible for this variation was the fact that the desert air was as empty of water in vapor form as the landscape was of water to drink. The liquid, if present in lakes and streams and vegetation, would not only have fed vapor into the air but would also have soaked up the midday heat for release into the night's chill air, moderating the temperatures in its vicinity.

For water—and this is another element of its unusualness—has a truly remarkable *heat capacity:* it

	NORMAL MELTING POINT		HEAT of FUSION		NORMAL BOILING POINT		HEAT of VAPORIZATION		SPECIFIC HEAT	
	°C	°F	Cal/g	BTU/lb	°C	°F	Cal/g	BTU/lb	Cal/g °C or BTU/lb °F	
ACETONE	-95	-139	23.4	42.2	56.5	133.7	124.5	224.1	0.506	at 0°C
ALCOHOL, ethyl	-117.3	-179.2	24.9	44.8	78.5	173.3	204	367.2	0.535	at 0°C
BENZENE	5.51	41.9	30.3	54.5	80.09	176.01	94.3	169.74	0.389	at 5°C
CARBON TETRACHLORIDE	-22.8	-9.04	4.16	7.48	76.8	170.3	46.4	83.52	0.198	at 0°C
MERCURY	-38.87	-37.96	2.82	5.07	356.58	673.88	70.6	127.08	0.03346	at 0°C
SULPHURIC ACID	-10.49	-5.09	24.0	43.2	330	626	122.1	219.78	0.270	at 0°C
TURPENTINE	—	—	—	—	159	318.2	68.6	123.48	0.411	at 0°C
WATER	0	32	79.71	143.4	100	212	539.55	971.19	1.007	at 0°C

FIG. 3. The physical properties of H_2O, compared in this chart with those of other substances, bear out the description of water as unusual. Note the high heats of fusion and vaporization and the high specific heat.

can absorb a great deal of heat without itself becoming (relatively) much warmer. Hang an empty pot above a hot fire and it will soon glow red-hot, but if that pot is filled with water and hung over the same fire for the same length of time, the temperature of the water may rise only a few degrees. ("The watched pot never boils," runs the adage, in recognition of the patience-taxing wait water's high heat capacity imposes on people who are in a hurry for their tea, or coffee, or steaming bath.) Vitally affecting the GIs in North Africa was the fact that water has some five times the heat capacity of sandy soil; the same amount of solar energy falling upon equal volumes of water and sandy soil will increase the temperature of the latter five times as much as it does the temperature of the former. Water's heat capacity, as a matter of fact, is the standard against which the heat capacities of other substances are commonly measured. One widely used unit for heat measurement is the *calorie*, which is the amount of heat required to raise the temperature of one gram of water from 14.5° C. to 15.5° C. Another commonly used unit is the *British thermal unit* (B.T.U.), defined as the amount of heat required to raise the temperature of a pound of water from 63° F. to 64° F. The heat capacity of a gram, or pound, or of any other unit weight of a substance is called its *specific heat* (Fig. 3), and since this is usually expressed in units of calories per gram per degree centigrade, or in units of B.T.U. per pound per degree Fahrenheit, water has a specific heat of 1. Sand, which has one fifth the heat capacity of water, has, by that token, a specific heat of 0.2, while iron, with one tenth of water's heat capacity, has a specific heat of 0.107.

Closely associated with water's unusual heat capacity are its equally unusual *latent heats of fusion and evaporation* (Fig. 4). We have remarked that when

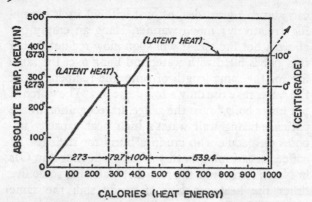

FIG. 4.   *The latent heats of H_2O are plotted in this graph. At the melting point one gram of water absorbs 79.7 calories without a rise in temperature. At the vaporization point one gram of water absorbs 539.4 calories before its temperature rises again.*

a solid substance's temperature is raised to the melting point, or when a liquid substance is at the boiling point, there is a pause, a transition stage, during which the two phases (solid and liquid, or liquid and vapor) coexist. During this interval of time, which lasts until the solid is completely liquefied or the liquid completely vaporized, heat, as we have said, is absorbed without producing any change whatever in the substance's temperature. This heat is called *latent,* and it varies in amount with different substances. Water's latent heats are uniquely high, a fact which adds greatly to its vital effect upon the surface temperatures of the earth.

Our use of the word "latent" recognizes a concept which, though implicit in what we have said, should be explicitly emphasized: the heat soaked up by water is not thereby destroyed. Basic to science, as you know, is the principle of the *conservation of energy,* which in its most general form states that energy may be transformed from one type to another (from heat to mechanical work, for instance) without loss, and that in a closed system the total amount of energy remains constant. This principle is sustained, of course, in the present instance. When we say that water has a remarkable heat capacity, we are saying simply that water substance can store more heat energy with less atomic and molecular agitation (which is what temperature measures) than any other widely prevalent substance. The energy is still there, in the water; it will be released as heat when the temperature of the immediate environment goes down, as we have already said; the temperature fall will thus be moderated.

To illustrate: Most of you know that on a night of freezing cold a tub of water keeps a greenhouse warmer than the outside air, even though some of the water freezes. There is a warming effect because water in the process of freezing releases the same amount of heat that it absorbs in the process of melting. We all know that we are far more uncomfortable on muggy days with temperatures in the low 90s than we are on clear dry days having temperatures several degrees higher. The reason is twofold: First, our perspiration in evaporating would cool us by absorbing heat from our skin and the immediately adjacent air, but it cannot evaporate in the water-saturated atmosphere of a muggy day. Second, the condensation of vapor into liquid releases heat in the precise amount that the vaporization of liquid absorbs it. And in both these cases—that of freezing and that of condensation—the amount of heat given off by water substance is (we repeat) higher than that given off by any other widely prevalent substance at the same points of phase change. (See Figs. 3 and 4.)

Many and various are the practical uses made of water's abnormally high latent heats, the most com-

mon being the use of ice for refrigeration (as ice
melts in an insulated box it drains heat from the substances we want cooled) and of water in air-cooling
systems (hot dry air passing across a wet surface gives
up much of its heat energy to change water liquid to
water vapor). Ancient people used the principle of
the modern air cooler—they cooled their drinking water by storing it in a porous vessel. Water's latent
heats are also responsible for one of the most awesome displays of power across summer skies, the sudden boiling up of huge cauliflower cumulus clouds
on a sultry afternoon. Though you may not have
known the scientific explanation of the phenomenon,
you who have witnessed this spectacle (and who has
not?) must have been impressed by the release of immense and turbulent heat energy into the upper air
in the condensation of invisible water vapor into visible water droplets.

Other Unusual Properties of Water

But the peculiarities of water as physical substance
are not limited to its heat relations. Equally remarkable and important to living processes is the fact that
water, of all natural substances, comes closest to being the universal *chemical solvent*. Almost any substance can be dissolved in water.

And here again we must define terms. We spoke
of the three forms or types of water—the solid, the
liquid, the gaseous—as phases of water, thus indicating that a "phase," as physical chemists use the word,
means a part of a system which is homogeneous and
separated from other parts at physical boundaries. A
solution is a phase consisting of two or more substances, one of which contains the others and is called
the *solvent* of them. The dissolved substances, distributed evenly throughout the solvent, are called *sol-*

utes. A mixture of oil and water is not a solution because it is not homogeneous: it consists of two phases, one being the droplets of oil, the other the body of water in which the droplets are suspended. A mixture of common table salt (sodium chloride, NaCl) and water, on the other hand, is a solution because it is homogeneous: the salt crystals are separated for the most part into tiny electrically charged particles called "ions," which are evenly distributed throughout the H_2O, and the two chemically different substances form a single physical phase.

And water, we stress, stands alone in its capacity as chemical solvent. About half the known chemical elements—many of them in abundance, some of them only in traces—have been found dissolved in natural waters. Every lake and stream in nature is a solution, and the oceans of the world are enormous and quite concentrated aqueous solutions of literally thousands of substances in ionic form, metals as well as non-metals, organic as well as inorganic compounds. Moreover, water is an *inert* solvent in that it is not itself changed chemically by most of the substances it dissolves. "This is important biologically," writes Robert E. Coker,[7] "because the materials required by living matter . . . can be delivered to the organisms in relatively unmodified form; the water itself . . . can be used as a solvent over and over again." Indeed, it was water's unique properties as an almost universal and inert solvent that enabled the sea to become the *magna mater,* or Great Mother, of all life. It was in the salt bath of the sea that the first living cells were formed, and it was only when the needed salt solution was internalized after hundreds of millions of years of evolutionary development that life could emerge from the sea onto solid land and

[7] In his *Streams, Lakes, Ponds* (University of North Carolina Press, 1954) page 7.

into the upper air. The functions formerly served by the sea were thereafter served by tissue fluids, blood plasma, the liquids which flow in cell interiors.

Yet another peculiarity of water is that, with the single exception of mercury, it has the highest *surface tension* (Plate I) of all commonly occurring liquids.

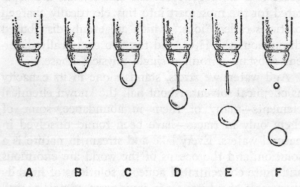

A B C D E F

FIG. 5. *Dripping water forms a succession of spheres as it dribbles from a faucet. A manifestation of unusually high surface tension, the phenomenon is pictured here in its stages.*

What is surface tension? You see it manifested whenever you watch water slowly dripping from a faucet. A film of water slowly bulges from the faucet, as if it were a thin rubber membrane stretching under a liquid weight. This membrane-like film gradually elongates as its upper edge clings to the faucet's rim until, suddenly, the weight is too great. The membrane does not break, however, as an overburdened sheet of rubber might do. Instead, it "lets go" of the faucet rim and snaps around a small quantity of water to form a freely falling drop which, as you doubtless have observed and possibly wondered about, is always almost spherical. (See Fig. 5.) In the absence of external pressure it would be perfectly spherical.

What you witness here is one example of water's abnormally strong tendency to "stick to itself" and "pull itself together," or to *cohere*; the water dripped from a faucet can most closely pull itself together by becoming a sphere, the sphere being of all possible shapes the one having the least surface for a given volume.

By cohesion, a tension is created at the water's surface in the sense that physical force, and an astonishing amount of it, is required to tear the surface apart. Unbroken, the surface can support objects much heavier than water—a needle, for instance, or a razor blade, or certain insects which run on liquid water as if the liquid were solid. As for the force required to pull apart a column of water (a substance's resistance to such force is its "tensile strength"), it is almost incredibly huge. Scientists have calculated from precise measurements of surface tension that a force of approximately 210,000 pounds would be required to rupture a column of perfectly pure, flawlessly structured water having a diameter of one inch! This is a highly theoretical figure, since there is no perfect water anywhere in the world. Every actual unit of water has structural flaws as well as dissolved gases which produce weakening bubbles, but a practical limit of 2000 pounds a square inch has been reached in laboratories—a tensile strength close to that of some steels.

Not only does liquid water cohere or stick to itself; it also *adheres* or sticks to other substances, solid substances, with which it comes in contact. It stuck to the faucet rim in our illustration. The degree of its adhesion, however, varies greatly among different substances. Water does not adhere to paraffin, for example—a fact expressed by saying that water does not "wet" a paraffin surface. (In a later chapter, we discuss "wetting" in physical-chemistry terms.) Water does adhere strongly to (or wet) glass, cotton fabric, common rocks and clays, nearly every particle of organic and inorganic matter forming soil, and so on.

Now when a highly cohesive liquid like water comes in contact with a solid surface to which it strongly adheres, the surface tension, which is a manifestation of cohesion, serves as a kind of membrane by which the body of the liquid is (so to speak) taken hold of and lifted by the adhesive force. Thus that portion of the water surface in direct contact with the glass wall of a fair-sized container is, as you may have noticed, perceptibly higher than the rest of the liquid surface. The edge of the water is quite evidently climbing up or being pulled up the glass wall. And the smaller the cross section of the container, the more clearly visible the upward pulling effect becomes. In a chemistry test tube the water surface is noticeably concave,[8] and in a glass tube of very fine bore the combination of surface tension with adhesive force may lift the enclosed column of water to quite remarkable heights.[9] This phenomenon, which is of major biological importance, is known as "capillary action" or "capillarity." It has much to do with the circulation of water in the soil, of vital solutions through the roots and stems of plants (though the principal cause here is a process known as osmotic pressure), and of blood through the human body.

[8] Mercury, whose surface tension is even higher than water's, does *not* wet (or adhere to) glass. Instead, it shrinks away from a glass wall in the same way as water shrinks away from a surface of paraffin, so that a depression rather than an elevation is formed at the plane of contact of the two substances. Hence mercury in a fine tube presents to the upper air a convex rather than a concave surface and in a fine-bored glass tube it is pulled down rather than up.

[9] *Soap Bubbles*, by C. V. Boys (Science Study Series, Doubleday, 1959), pages 32–33.

CHAPTER 2

The Discovery of Water

The Nature of Scientific Discovery

If you questioned our use of "unusual" in the introduction to this book you may be questioning our use of "discovery" in the title of the present chapter. For uncounted eons before the first living matter appeared on earth, water was as prevalent over the earth's face as it now is. The earliest men used it and probably thought they "knew" it. How, then, can we speak of the *discovery* of water, as if this substance were a rare and hidden element like radium?

Obviously, we are using the term in a special way, as we have the word "unusual." We use it quite deliberately, in fact, to indicate the nature of science as an investigative method and the nature of the knowledge this method develops.

There is a very accurate sense in which science may be described as a voyage of discovery. At the outset the scientist stands on familiar shores amidst objects and phenomena known to him. But he does not take these objects and phenomena for granted; he refuses to assume that the immediate appearance of a natural thing or event—the initial impress it makes on his unaided senses—is its total and final reality. He begins to ask questions about it and so embarks on a questing voyage into the unknown. Moreover, the questions he asks are asked in a rigorously objective way. They demand answers equally objective in that these do not derive from the scientist's individual personality and temperament and are wholly independent of his personal desires, religious beliefs, moral judgments, private fears, and so on. This amounts to saying that the scientific voyage is not a quest for the unique but, instead, a quest for the general. By ruling out of account all the elements of his experience which are exclusively his own—all that derive wholly or partly from his feeling self, all that depend solely upon his unique spatial and temporal position—the scientist insures that the answers he obtains to his questions can be precisely duplicated by any other human being who places himself in precisely similar circumstances.

We have mentioned radium, whose discovery by Pierre and Marie Curie is one of the popular epics of scientific history. This particular voyage had as its immediate object the discovery of the source of mysterious rays which, emitted from uranium and even more strongly from the mineral pitchblende (it contains uranium), fogged photographic plates and caused electric conductivity in gases through which they passed. But the Curies' isolation of radium and two other hitherto unknown radioactive elements, polonium and actinium, was not the ultimate end of this voyage. Far more important than the elements themselves was the phenomenon of radioactivity which they manifested. It was the shaping and rigorous testing of theories concerning this phenomenon, coupled with Albert Einstein's momentous concept of the equivalence of mass and energy, that brought us, for good or evil, to the Atomic Age. The end of the voyage in which the Curies participated, in other words, was not a specific thing; it was a general law.

And this is the end sought by all scientific quests, ultimately. Webster's Dictionary is almost as precise as it is succinct when it defines "science" as "accumulated knowledge systematized and formulated with reference to the discovery of general truths or the operation of general laws." The only possible improvement on this would be to stress that the aim is not "accumulated knowledge" as a compendium of physical facts but, instead, the general truths and laws by which the facts are informed and systematically related to one another. And to this we must at once add that the aim or end is never finally achieved, as we emphasized in our introduction to this book. The general truths of science are never absolutes. Always they are tentative, subject to revision as new experimental observations are made and new concepts developed. Always, too, this revision is toward a greater simplicity and generalization whereby phenomena hitherto unrelated conceptually are recognized as aspects of a single, unified, and continuously evolving Truth.

So it has been with regard to water.

Fire and Water

For some two thousand years after Western science and philosophy were born, with Thales, into ancient Greece, water was accepted as a basic element of the universe. Thales himself, as we have seen, regarded it as *the* basic element of which everything is made. Empedocles, a Greek philosopher born a century after Thales, modified this conception. He postulated the existence of four basic elements—fire, air, water, and earth—and of two moving forces—love and strife. From these, he said, all that exists is made and all that happens in nature may be explained. Not until methods of chemical analysis, qualitative and quantitative, were developed in the eighteenth century was it proved that not one of Empedocles' "elements" was truly elementary and that fire could not properly be termed a "substance" at all.

Indeed, it was the effort to sustain the alleged elemental nature of fire against a growing body of hostile evidence that incited the first long steps toward the discovery of water as we now know it.

Obvious to all from very ancient times was the fact that some substances burn in air (are combustible) whereas others do not (are non-combustible). Less obvious, but quickly apparent to accurate observation, is the fact that, among combustible substances, some disappear from sight and touch as they burn, leaving an ash weighing much less than the original stuff, whereas others burn into an ash which is actually heavier than the original substance. Particularly is this last true of metallic substances. These, when strongly heated, are transformed into what in the seventeenth century were called "calxes" (we recognize them as metallic oxides), whose weight is often very much greater than that of the metals before heating. Moreover, the process may sometimes be reversed by burning the calx (iron oxide, for instance) in a mixture with charcoal: when this is done, the calx is transformed into the original and lighter metal from which it was made. How explain this phenomenon?

The German chemist G. E. Stahl (1660–1734) had a partial and initially plausible explanation to offer. He postulated the existence of a "material and principle of fire," which he distinguished from "fire itself" and named *phlogiston*. Charcoal, he assumed, was almost pure phlogiston: When calxes were heated in the presence of carbon, they absorbed phlogiston; during the calcining (forming of calxes) of metals, phlogiston was dispelled. Stahl did not concern himself with the weight changes occurring in combustion, but his immediate successors had to face up to the fact. Their solution was to endow phlogiston with a truly remarkable property—phlogiston, they hypothesized, had "negative weight." It was endowed, in other words, with the very opposite of weight, a property of levity or lightness. (Since flames always rise, the ancient Greeks had attributed the same quality to fire.) Thus, when phlogiston was added to a substance, the substance lost weight. Subtract phlogiston from the substance and the substance gained weight.

This theory, absurd as it seems to modern eyes, remained, nevertheless, a basic and almost universally accepted tenet of chemistry for a century. Nor were its effects on the developing science all bad. The search for Stahl's mysterious fire principle stimulated the development of increasingly precise laboratory apparatus and techniques, many of which remain integral to quantitative and qualitative analysis in chemistry today. It also stimulated experiments and theoretical explanations of their results which opened the way to our present knowledge of what water is and why it behaves as it does.

For instance, phlogiston manifested its amazing properties only in the presence of air. A calx was not formed if the metal was heated in a vacuum. Why was this? The question caused several first-rate minds to focus their attention on air as a subject of scientific study, and they soon were conducting experiments through which this supposedly simple and basic element, one of the four of Empedocles, was found to be not simple at all but highly complex.

Often, of course, and indeed for the most part, the experiments did not focus directly on the question we have phrased. The afore-mentioned Joseph Black was not directly concerned with it when, in the mid-eighteenth century, as a medical student in Glasgow, Scotland, he carried out a series of epoch-making experiments with "calcerous earths" (lime). If the question had not aroused an interest in air, however, Black might have paid no heed to the particular kind of "air" which bubbled through an acid he poured over chalk. As it was, he devised experiments to measure the quantities and properties of the "air" thus obtained, finding (*a*) that it would not support combustion (nothing would burn in its presence alone); (*b*) that it occurred as a small constituent of atmospheric air and could be removed by bubbling air through limewater, forming a chalky precipitate in such water; (*c*) that it was a product of the fermentation of beer; (*d*) that it was a product of the combustion of charcoal; and (*e*) that it was expired from the lungs as a man breathed. Black called this gas "fixed air"; we recognize it as carbon dioxide.

Shortly thereafter another important gas was isolated. Actually the existence of this gas had been demonstrated long before Black began his work—several decades before Stahl had developed the phlogiston theory, as a matter of fact. The great Robert Boyle (1627–91), the English natural philosopher who is generally deemed the father of chemistry, had observed and recorded his observation that when iron filings were treated with a mineral acid a highly inflammable "air" was emitted. But it remained for another Englishman, Henry Cavendish (1731–1810), to apply, in the mid-1760s, methods by which this "inflammable air," as he called it, could be obtained in pure form and its properties described. He poured sulfuric acid over pieces of zinc (or hydrochloric acid over tin; the effect was the same), collecting the emitted gas in a water-filled cylindrical glass vessel inverted in a tank of water. Since the cylindrical container had been filled with water, all the air had been forced out of it. Cavendish let the gas from the zinc and acid bubble up into this container and thus collected a sample in pure form. The sample proved to be so violently combustible when in the presence of air that Cavendish, contrasting it with Black's "fixed air" and presuming that it came from the metal, identified it with phlogiston. We know this gas as hydrogen.

Cavendish announced his discovery in 1766. Some five years later a brilliant Frenchman named Antoine-Laurent Lavoisier (1743–94) embarked on a momentous experimental study of the combustion and calcination (the formation of calxes) of metals. He was particularly struck by the large increase in weight that accompanied the burning of phosphorus in air, and he refused to accept the explanation that this increase resulted from the driving off of phlogiston with its fantastic negative weight. He preferred to assume —and indeed it seemed to him clearly evident—that the phosphorus gained weight because it took up something from the air in which it was heated. What was this "something"? A clue was provided in February of 1774, when a French chemist named Bayen reported the results of some experiments he had made with red calx (red oxide) of mercury. This red powder has certain remarkable properties, one of which Bayen noted. He heated the calx alone (that is, without mixing it with charcoal) to a temperature just below "red heat" and found that a gas was given off and pure mercury recovered. The gas was "fixed air," announced Bayen, who apparently had given it scant inspection if he examined it at all. Soon thereafter Lavoisier began to conduct experiments of his own with the red mercury calx, but, unlike Bayen, he paid close attention to the emitted gas. Whatever it might be, he saw at once, this "air" was not "fixed." A candle placed in "fixed air" was promptly extinguished; one placed in the red-calx "air" burned more brightly.

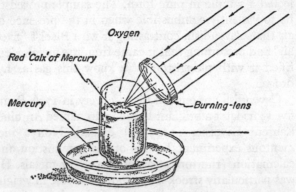

Oxygen

Red 'Calx' of Mercury

Mercury

Burning-lens

FIG. 6.   *Priestley's experiment separated red calx into mercury and air that was not "fixed." As he wrote in* Experiments and Observations (1775), *"But having afterwards procured a lens of twelve inches diameter, and twenty inches focal distance, I proceeded with great alacrity to examine, by the help of it, what kind of air a great variety of substances, natural and factitious, would yield, putting them into . . . vessels . . . which I filled with quicksilver and kept inverted in a basin of the same . . . on the 1st of August, 1774, I endeavored to extract the air from mercurius calcinatus per se; and I presently found. . . ." Apparently he left no drawing of his apparatus, but this figure illustrates the scheme.*

Meanwhile, across the Channel, Joseph Priestley (1733–1804), the English chemist, was also experimenting with the red calx of mercury. A few months after Bayen's announcement, of which he may have known nothing, and several months before Lavoisier began to work with this calx, Priestley placed the red powder in a sealed retort, heated it with a burning glass, and bubbled the emitted gas through water as Cavendish had done when he discovered "inflammable air." (Fig. 6.) He, too, tested with a candle the "air" thus isolated and found that it supported combustion. Therefore it could not be "fixed air." It might, however, be "laughing gas" (nitrous oxide), whose strange effects upon those who inhaled it had by then been widely observed—and Priestley at first assumed that it was. He was still of this opinion when, two months later, he visited Paris and told Lavoisier of this most recent of his researches, stimulating the latter to initiate new studies along the same lines.

Now it is a fact of history, interesting in itself and significant of the nature of scientific discovery, that Bayen was by no means the first man to observe that the heating of mercury's red calx resulted in the giving off of a gas, leaving pure mercury behind. An alchemist named De Sultzbach had done the same (he called the emitted gas a "spirit") as early as 1489! His observation, however, was no more than another random fact among ten thousand noted by medieval alchemists in their search for the "philosopher's stone." This "stone," you will recall, was a magical something which would enable the alchemist to transmute base metals into gold, cure all human ills, and achieve for himself all manner of supernatural powers. Not until the same phenomenon was observed by rigorously disciplined minds in quest, not of magical powers, but of objective truths based on causal reasoning did the observation begin to bear fruit. Priestley, being a skilled laboratory technician and a precise observer, did the groundwork. As for Lavoisier, he was not only a skilled technician but also remarkably free of theoretical prejudice and was able to focus upon his observations a rare brilliance of logic and creative imagination.

It is a further interesting and significant fact that neither Priestley nor Lavoisier was actually the first man to isolate and study scientifically the gas which they obtained from the mercury calx. The great Swedish chemist Karl Wilhelm Scheele (1742–86) isolated it in 1772 or 1773, calling the new gas "fire air." However, the manuscript of his book *Air and Fire*, wherein he first reported this work, was not sent to the printers until 1775 and was not published until two years later, and his observations remained wholly unknown to the English and French scientists as they conducted their crucial experiments. James Bryant Conant points to this fact in Case 2 of the *Harvard Case Histories in Experimental Science* (Harvard University Press, 1957, Vol. I) as an illustration of the importance of swift and accurate communication among scientists. Such communication prevents needlessly repetitious error and insures exploitation of discovered fact. The communication failure between Scheele and his fellow scientists in other lands robbed him of his due reward. It also made his work marginal to, and ineffective within, the mainstream of scientific progress, as were for the same reason nearly all the brilliant insights and investigations of Leonardo da Vinci (1452–1519) in the late fifteenth and early sixteenth centuries.

Between Lavoisier and Priestley, on the other hand, there was (as we have seen) constant and mutually stimulating communication whereby each learned from the other's mistakes as well as from the other's triumphs. For instance, following their meeting in Paris in October of 1774, the Englishman and the Frenchman conducted simultaneously the same experiment with the "air" emitted from the mercury calx and made, at first, the same error of interpretation. Priestley swiftly corrected his mistake. Lavoisier did not until Priestley pointed the error out to him, but the Frenchman saw at once the discovery's deathly significance for the phlogiston theory, whereas Priestley clung to this theory, being apparently emotionally committed to it, for as long as he lived. Conant tells the story fully in Case 2, presenting it as a classic example of the role "chance" or "accident" often plays in the making of scientific discoveries and as an example, too, of the necessity to revise or reject general theories, no matter how old and well established, whenever accurately observed facts contradict them. Equally necessary to progress, in such cases, is the development of new general theories, whereby the freshly discovered truth may be discerned as logically consistent with all the other known truths to which it can be related.

But the interested reader is urged to consult Conant's account for the details of all this. Suffice it here to say that two or three years before he began his work with the mercury calx, Priestley had devised a chemical test of the "goodness" of atmospheric air. By "goodness" he meant the ability of the air to support combustion and the respiration of animals, and he believed it to be equivalent to the *absence* of phlogiston. To the extent that the air lacked phlogiston, it could absorb this fire principle from a heated substance or a breathing animal, but when it became saturated with phlogiston and could hold no more, it became thoroughly "bad." This "saturated" air put out candles and smothered animals.

Priestley's test made use of "nitrous air." We know this gas as nitric oxide, having the chemical formula NO. Priestley knew it as a colorless "air" which produced "red fumes" when mixed with ordinary air. By experiment he had found that the pure colorless "nitrous air" was insoluble in water, whereas the "red fumes" (nitrous oxide, N_2O) dissolved readily, and that the "red fumes" were not formed in enclosed air where a candle had been burned until the flame went out. He had also found that the "best" air he knew of—the purest atmospheric air—could be made thoroughly "bad" if it were mixed with enough "nitrous air" over water in an enclosed space—the formation and dissolving of the "red fumes" in such circumstances had precisely the same effect as the burning of a candle. Moreover, the process was accompanied by a reduction in the volume[1] of the air remaining above the water. All this suggested to Priestley his method of measuring air's "goodness" in quantitative terms. He found that the maximum reduction in volume occurred when he mixed one volume of "nitrous air" with two volumes of the "best" ordinary air. The reduction, indeed, was quite astonishingly large: within minutes, the original three volumes (one of "nitrous air," two of the "best" atmospheric air) were reduced to approximately 1.8 volumes—20 per cent less than the volume of the atmospheric air alone before the "nitrous air" was added. But when one volume of "nitrous air" was mixed with two volumes of

[1] You may be puzzled by our use of "volume" here, remembering that in our definition of a *gas* in Chapter 1 we said that it has neither rigidity nor definite volume. Its volume, we said, is that of its container. But suppose that the container is a cylinder having a piston in it (like a pump) whereby a precisely measurable pressure can be exerted upon a precisely measurable volume of gas. In that case, the volume of the gas will be found to vary *inversely* with the pressure upon it: the greater the pressure, the smaller the volume, and vice versa, provided the temperature of the gas remains constant. The relationship between pressure and volume with regard to gases is expressed in one of the basic equations of physics:

$$\frac{V_1}{V} = \frac{P}{P_1}$$

where P refers to the smaller pressure and V to the volume of an ideal gas under that pressure and P_1 refers to the greater pressure and V_1 to the volume of the ideal gas under that pressure. This is called Boyle's Law, after the great Boyle whose early observation of hydrogen we have mentioned. Hence, when we speak here of a reduction in the *volume* of gas, we're assuming a constant pressure upon that gas; a reduction in the substantial amount of gas in the container will be accompanied by a proportionate reduction in the gas's volume if the pressure upon it remains the same, according to Boyle's Law.

the "worst" ordinary air over water, there was no reduction in volume whatever; three volumes of gas remained. Thus the limits of "goodness" and "badness" in terms of "nitrous air" were established, and there were intermediate grades of "goodness" to which quantitative values could be assigned. Priestley had published a report of all this in 1772.

Now the fact that the "air" derived from the mercury calx would support combustion suggested, inevitably, the application of Priestley's "nitrous air" test to this new "air." Both Priestley and Lavoisier tried the experiment in late 1774 or early 1775. They found that the total amount of "air" was diminished from three volumes to 1.6 volumes when one of "nitrous air" was mixed with two of the new "air"—a diminution only slightly greater (about 8 per cent) than that occurring when the test was applied to the "best" ordinary air. Both men noted this difference in diminution; neither regarded it, at the outset, as substantially significant. On the contrary, since the calx-derived "air" supported combustion (if somewhat more strongly than ordinary air) and was diminished by "nitrous air" in only a slightly greater proportion than was atmospheric air, the two scientists initially assumed that the calx-derived "air" actually was ordinary air, though a "better" sample of it than had ever before been obtained. Lavoisier indicated as much in his first report of his experiment, read before the French Academy of Sciences at its Easter meeting in 1775 and famous in the history of science as his "Easter Memoir."

Before Lavoisier had presented his paper, however, Priestley "by accident," as he himself stresses in his report, had made an astonishing and exciting discovery. One day in March 1775, having completed a "nitrous air" test on the calx-derived "air," Priestley happened to have at hand a lighted candle, which, on sudden impulse, he thrust into the 1.6 volumes of "air" remaining above the water. The flame should at once have gone out; it would have done so had the original sample been ordinary air. As we now know, the proportionate mixture of NO with air which Priestley used would have resulted in a complete absorption of the oxygen (one fifth of ordinary air by volume) into the dissolved red gas, N_2O, leaving only inert nitrogen gas, which, with a tiny admixture of other gases, such as carbon dioxide ("fixed air"), makes up approximately four fifths of common air's volume. But the flame did not go out. Instead, it became more brilliant. And it kept on burning long after it should have been extinguished by (in Priestley's language) completely *phlogisticated* air. Obviously this calx-derived "air" was not ordinary; it was an "air" that was *dephlogisticated* (freed of phlogiston) to a greater degree than any Priestley had observed before.

In this he was abundantly confirmed by subsequent tests. For instance, a mouse placed in a limited amount of the new air lived longer than it could have done in ordinary air, and when "nitrous air" was mixed with the air the mouse had breathed, "red fumes" were formed as before and the total volume of air diminished. Indeed, Priestley found that whereas "common air takes about one half of its bulk from nitrous air before it begins to receive any addition to its dimensions from more nitrous air," this amazing *new* air "took more than four half-measures before it ceased to be diminished by more nitrous air, and even five half-measures made no addition to the original dimensions." He had made what Conant calls the "effective discovery" of oxygen—Scheele's anticipation of it being ineffective in scientific progress—and there is significant irony in the fact that

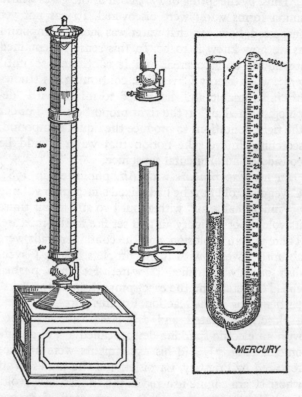

FIG. 7. The Volta eudiometer (left), a device for measuring the volumes of gases, was used by Henry Cavendish in studies of "inflammable air" and "dephlogisticated air." This drawing is taken from an old print. A modern eudiometer is drawn at the right.

Priestley continued to call it *dephlogisticated air* to the end of his days.

Thus, by the spring of 1775 both of the gases whose union forms water were discovered. It was not yet suspected, however, that water was such a compound as we now know it to be. In this sense it remained unknown, undiscovered, and it continued so until 1783, when Henry Cavendish, continuing his studies of "inflammable air," happened to mix it with "dephlogisticated air" in the right proportions and under the right conditions to produce the liquid compound, scotching forever the notion that water should be considered an elemental substance.

In his *Experiments with Air*, published in 1784, Cavendish told how he had mixed a measured volume of "inflammable air" with about two and a half times its volume of ordinary air and set fire to the mixture. There was an explosion, and the container walls were abruptly covered with liquid droplets. These Cavendish quickly identified as water. He then pushed ahead to determine the exact proportion of the "airs" participating in the reaction. For this purpose he used a closely graduated and calibrated tube equipped with an electric sparking device, called a Volta eudiometer (Fig. 7), and his experiments were at once repeated by Priestley, Lavoisier, and the James Watt whose steam engine ushered in the Industrial Revolution. Water, it was proved, is composed of oxygen and hydrogen in the proportions *by weight* of about eight to one. The proportions *by volume*, Sir Humphry Davy[2] found, were about two to one—two of hydrogen, one of oxygen.

But as we indicated at the opening of this chapter, and as was true in the search for radium, the ultimate end of this portion of the scientific voyage was not

[2] Davy used the newly discovered technique of electrolysis to take water apart.

the finding out of new physical facts, but, rather, the making of new, tentatively acceptable explanations. And if Priestley was the effective discoverer of oxygen and Cavendish of water as a chemical compound, Lavoisier was the man who devised the new and larger conceptual scheme whereby the freshly discovered truths were "explained" in terms of consistency with older truths, and whereby new paths toward fruitful research were clearly indicated.

Lavoisier recognized at once that the new "air," which he at first called "vital air," was the "something" which "combines with metals during calcination and increases their weight." This was tantamount to saying that burning is a process of oxidation. One proof of this was the fact, established experimentally by Lavoisier, that the heating of a metal in the presence of steam resulted in the formation of a calx (metallic oxide) and the release of free hydrogen. Though it was far from obvious to the older among Lavoisier's contemporaries, it was now perfectly plain to the great Frenchman that the assumed existence of a mysterious fire principle, phlogiston, was not only unnecessary but flatly self-contradictory. How could there be a "something" which was quantitatively less than nothing?

As a matter of fact, Lavoisier published the death warrant of Stahl's theory in 1783, almost, if not quite, simultaneously with Cavendish's discovery of the nature of water as physical substance. Lavoisier's paper of that year, *Reflections on Phlogiston*, laid several of the foundation stones of that conceptual edifice soon known as the "new" chemistry, and with the publication six years later of his epoch-making *Elementary Treatise in Chemistry*, he firmly established the bases of the new edifice. He presented four general principles or laws: (1) substances burn only when "vital air" is present; (2) all non-metals when

burned in air give rise to acids; (3) a metal burned
in air forms a calx by combining with "vital air" and
becomes heavier in the process; (4) there is no such
thing as phlogiston. In addition, he proposed a new
chemical nomenclature—essentially the one we use
today. "Vital air" became oxygen (from the Greek
oxys, "acid," and the root of *gignesthai*, "to be born").
"Inflammable air" became hydrogen, "the water producer." "Phlogisticated air" became nitrogen, "the
nitric-acid producer." Compounds of metals became
oxides instead of calxes; and salts of acids became sul-
fates, sulfites, nitrates, nitrites, and so on. As for
water, formed by the burning of hydrogen, it could
be termed, in the new nomenclature, the oxide of
hydrogen.

Even this, however, was not the end of the voyage.
It marked the completion of but one stage of it. The
next stage gave still wider and deeper answers to the
question "What is water?"—answers framed in terms
of atomic-molecular theory.

The Atoms of Democritus

In one sense, atomic theory is a very ancient concept. It was elaborated in philosophic terms by two
Greeks, Leucippus and Democritus, as long ago as
the fifth century B.C., and it may be that even these
early thinkers did not originate the idea. But these
two are generally regarded as the founders of materi-
alistic philosophy in the Western world, for they were
convinced, and published their conviction in ways
convincing to others, that the universe is made up
of extremely tiny particles of matter into which any
substance may (theoretically) be decomposed but
which are themselves solid, indivisible, and indestructible. This Greek theory, however, was purely speculative. Untested experimentally, it had only the pre-

carious external support of everyday observations, which could be, and were, interpreted very differently. The most influential philosophers of later Greece were, in fact, flatly opposed to atomism, arguing with a logical persuasiveness at least equal to Democritus's that the basic universal substance must be a continuous whole.

With the fall of Rome, the actual writings of Democritus and Leucippus were lost, and the atomism they espoused might also have been, had it not been summarized and credited to them by a Roman poet, Lucretius, who did his work some four centuries after they were dead. Lucretius's didactic poem *De Rerum Natura*, which survived the Middle Ages, became a potent influence upon European intellectual life as Western civilization's dark night gave way to the Renaissance, as alchemy gave way to chemistry, and materialism, after long centuries wholly dominated by idealistic and mystical theories, became again a widely effective philosophy. The great Isaac Newton, for example, who on foundations laid by Galileo and Kepler raised the towering structure of the physics bearing his name, was a thoroughgoing atomist. Wrote he in his *Opticks* (1706):

It seems probable to me that God in the beginning formed matter in solid, massy, hard, impenetrable, movable particles, of such sizes and figures, and with such other properties, and in such proportions to space as most conduce to the end for which he formed them; and that these primitive particles being solids, are incomparably harder than any porous bodies compounded of them; even so very hard as never to wear or break to pieces; no ordinary power being able to divide what God Himself made One, in the first creation.

Atomism contributed to the prevailing intellectual climate within which Priestley, Cavendish, and Lavoisier did their work, and it received support from Lavoisier's "new" chemistry. The latter, in fact, was directly responsible for one of the earliest translations of atomic theory from the realm of speculative philosophy to that of scientific hypothesis. In 1789, the English natural philosopher William Higgins, supporting Lavoisier's then brand-new oxygen theory, published A *Comparative View of the Phlogistic and Antiphlogistic Theories*, in which he outlined an atomic hypothesis.

But it was another Englishman, John Dalton (1766–1844), who is generally deemed the "father" of modern scientific atomism. He was the first to test the theory's validity through specific experiments in chemistry. By concentrating on atomic weights, he made the theory quantitative and amenable to laboratory test. In 1805, in the *Memoirs of the Literary and Philosophical Society of Manchester*, Dalton published a paper setting forth the following hypotheses: (1) all matter is composed of individual atoms which are indivisible and indestructible; (2) a chemical combination—such as hydrogen with oxygen to form water—represents an atom-to-atom linkage whose proportions of constituent substances can always be expressed in simple whole numbers; (3) the same volumes of different gases contain different numbers of atoms, and each gas's atoms are of a size peculiar to it; (4) atoms of different substances have different weights.

Dalton also introduced a symbolic device, highly useful, for representing chemical combinations. Each kind of atom was assigned by him a unique symbol. Thus oxygen ○ combined with hydrogen ⊙ to produce water ○ ⊙—from which it may be seen that, in Dalton's view, water's essential unit was a particle containing one atom of hydrogen and one of oxygen. Since it had been experimentally determined by this time that water was composed of 85⅔ per cent oxygen and 14⅓ per cent hydrogen, by weight, Dalton concluded (erroneously, as we now know) that the oxygen atom weighed six times as much as a hydrogen atom.

While Dalton was studying chemical combinations in terms of the *weights* of the combining substances, interpreting the results by his atomic theory and testing the latter by the former, a French chemist was studying such combinations in terms of the *volumes* of the combining substances, limiting his researches to substances in the gaseous phase and refraining from any application of atomic theory to his results. He so refrained, we suspect, because his results seemed to contradict a basic tenet of Dalton's theory.[3]

The Frenchman was Joseph Louis Gay-Lussac (1778–1850). He was a phenomenally skilled laboratory technician, his experimental talent greatly exceeding Dalton's. The springboard of his studies was Cavendish's discovery that approximately two volumes of hydrogen unite with one volume of oxygen to produce water. Gay-Lussac proved experimentally that the more accurate the measurements the closer the combination came to the two-to-one ratio, his closest approximation in the laboratory being a ratio of 1.9989 to 1. He thereupon concluded the actual ratio of combination was *precisely* two to one, since the very slight difference between the 2 volumes of hydrogen and 1.9989 volumes was well within the

[3] The informed reader will be aware that here, as in our discussion of the isolation of oxygen, the authors owe much to the *Case Histories in Experimental Science* (Harvard, 1957), issued in two volumes under the editorship of James Bryant Conant.

narrowest possible margin of experimental error. He
then went on to show by careful experiment that two
volumes of carbon monoxide unite with one volume
of oxygen to form two volumes of carbon dioxide,
that one volume of hydrogen and one of chlorine produce two volumes of hydrogen chloride, and so on.
Always, when two gases combined chemically, they
did so in a volume bearing a simple ratio to the original volume, an observation summed up in what became known as the "law of combining volumes." Gay-
Lussac himself put it as follows in his original report,
published in 1809: ". . . the compounds of gaseous
substance with each other are always formed in very
simple ratios, so that, representing one of the terms by
unity, the other is 1, or 2, or at most 3. These ratios
by volume are not observed with solid or liquid substances, nor when we consider weights."

The latter point—the fact that the volume ratios
and the weight ratios of combining gases were of a
wholly different order, so that one set of ratios could
not in Dalton's conception be rendered consistent
with the other set—deeply disturbed the English
scientist.

Gay-Lussac's results, interpreted by atomic theory,
seemed clearly to indicate that equal volumes of different gases contain equal numbers of atoms or combinations of atoms (molecules)—equal numbers of
particles, in other words. Consider, for example, the
case of "nitrous air," now known as nitric oxide
(NO). If one volume of nitrogen unites with an
equal volume of oxygen to produce the nitric oxide,
then obviously there were precisely as many atoms of
oxygen as there were atoms of nitrogen in the original
equal volumes. Similarly with chlorine and hydrogen
when they combined to form hydrogen chloride, and
with several other combining gases. The conclusion
that equal volumes of gases, no matter how different

in kind, always contain equal numbers of particles seemed inescapable. For it is a basic and necessary assumption of science that natural phenomena follow rigidly prescribed patterns. If one discovers the pattern, one can predict the phenomenon, and it would be (at least apparently) a violation of this natural order to assume that the "equal volumes–equal numbers" rule applied in every instance where precise determinations could be made without applying in all instances. Moreover, the rule was consistent with many other inferences drawn from experimental observations of the behavior of gases. It was therefore accepted by many of Gay-Lussac's scientific contemporaries.

It was not accepted by all, however. Most emphatically it was not accepted by John Dalton.

You may recall the third of the four Dalton hypotheses which we summarized on page 56. He reiterated it in his *New System of Chemical Philosophy*, published in 1810, asserting as a maxim "that every species of pure elastic fluid [i.e., gas] has its particles globular and of a size; and that no two species agree in the size of their particles." In his scheme, this amounted to saying that "no two species" could "agree" in the number of particles contained in equivalent volumes. He conceived the structure of gases to be similar to that of a pile of shot wherein each "particle," or (to be precise) the "atmosphere of heat" with which he believed each particle to be surrounded, was in actual contact with the "atmospheres" of its neighbors. Obviously, the larger the diameter of the particles, the smaller the number that could be packed into any given space. He went so far as to work out from his conception of gaseous structure the presumed diameters of the "ultimate particles" of different gases and, on that reckoning, the relative numbers of these particles that could be

contained in a given volume. Since the particle diameters by his calculations varied widely among the
different gases, so did the number of particles in
equivalent volumes of those gases.

Dalton concluded that Gay-Lussac's ratios of combining volumes were crude approximations, Gay-Lussac having rounded out his numbers in impermissible
ways. For instance, Dalton calculated that the numbers of atoms of oxygen and nitrogen in equal volumes of the two gases stood in a ratio of 1 to 0.833
rather than 1 to 1; the actual combining volumes,
therefore, in the formation of nitric oxide, must be
0.833 of oxygen with 1 of nitrogen (obviously the reaction would cease when all the particles of nitrogen
were used up) instead of the 1-to-1 ratio which Gay-
Lussac had asserted.

And even if one rejected Dalton's "shot pile"
analogy, as many of his contemporaries did (it is a
grossly inaccurate model of gaseous structure), one
encountered serious objections to the "equal volumes
–equal numbers" rule. Consider the combination of
oxygen and hydrogen to form water in its gaseous
phase. Each "ultimate particle" of water as steam
must certainly be heavier than each atom of oxygen,
since water is a compound of oxygen and hydrogen.
Yet steam is actually lighter than oxygen! The only
possible explanation of this seemed to be that there
were fewer particles of steam in a given volume than
there were particles of oxygen in the equal volume.
Similarly with carbon monoxide, which is lighter than
oxygen despite the fact that every one of its "particles" consists of an atom of oxygen plus an atom of
carbon; with ammonia, which is lighter than nitrogen,
though it is a compound of nitrogen and hydrogen;
and with many other compound gases, each of which
is lighter than one of its chemical constituents. In
every such case, said Dalton, there must be a smaller

number of particles in a volume of the compounded gas than there was in an equal volume of the heavier constituent gas.

Yet another cogent objection derived from the fact that, in instance after instance, the volume of the gas produced through the reaction of the two gases exceeded the volume of at least one of the latter. Thus, according to Gay-Lussac, one volume of oxygen combined with two volumes of hydrogen to produce precisely two volumes of water vapor. But how could this be if a volume of water vapor (steam) contained precisely the same number of particles as an equal volume of oxygen? Since each particle of vapor contains at least one oxygen atom, each of the two volumes of vapor must contain only *half* as many particles (molecules of oxygen-with-hydrogen) as the equal original volume of oxygen contained. The conclusion could be avoided only by assuming that each atom of oxygen in the original volume split in two as it reacted with hydrogen—an assumption which, if accepted, invalidated the very essence of atomic theory as Dalton and Newton conceived it. Atoms by definition were ultimate and indivisible particles, "so very hard as never to wear or break to pieces," and the experimental evidence that this was a definition of truth seemed overwhelming. How otherwise "explain" the "laws" of definite, multiple, and equivalent proportions of combining substances which had, by this time, been clearly established?

So an impasse was reached.

We have indicated before, but cannot too often reiterate, that in science, as in all other intellectual endeavors, the ultimate test of truth is consistency. It is wholly impossible for the human mind to accept as equally true propositions which contradict one another. If two of them do so, one or both must be modified to make the two consistent with one another and with all other established truth—either that or both must be rejected as false. In the present case, it was Dalton's conception that was modified, though Dalton himself never accepted the modification.

In a paper published in 1811, an Italian physicist named Amedeo Avogadro de Querengna (1776–1856) made a highly ingenious proposal for reconciling the "equal volumes–equal numbers" rule (which he accepted) with the postulated indivisibility of the atom. The contradictions between the two all arose from the assumption that the indivisible atom was the unit component—the basic "particle"—of gaseous elements. Certainly this assumption seemed plausible at first glance, but it was by no means necessary, and, since it led to grave difficulties, it must be abandoned. In place of it Avogadro proposed that the "particles" of gaseous elements, as of gaseous compounds, were not single atoms but, rather, groups of atoms joined together in what he called "constituent molecules." What happened when two elementary gases reacted with one another was not a process of atom splitting but a process of molecule splitting, he went on—and the truth of his assumption seemed to him "proved" by the way in which it removed every objection Dalton himself had raised to the clear implications of the Gay-Lussac experiments.

Take, for example, the reaction in which one volume of oxygen combines with two volumes of hydrogen to produce water. Assume for the moment that each "particle" of oxygen and each of hydrogen consists, not of a single atom, but of a double atom—two atoms joined in molecules which we designate as O_2 and H_2—and that there are precisely n (for the same number of) molecules in each of equal volumes of the two gaseous elements. The reaction of the two gases to produce water then becomes as follows:

$$1 \text{ volume oxygen} + 2 \text{ volumes hydrogen} \longrightarrow$$
$$2 \text{ volumes water vapor}$$
$$OR$$
$$n \text{ particles oxygen} + 2n \text{ particles hydrogen} \longrightarrow$$
$$2n \text{ particles vapor}$$
$$OR$$
$$nO_2 + 2nH_2 \longrightarrow n[H_4O_2] \longrightarrow 2nH_2O$$
$$OR$$
$$(\text{to simplify})$$
$$O_2 + 2H_2 \longrightarrow H_4O_2 \longrightarrow 2H_2O*$$

The integrity of the atom is maintained by this assumption, and the fact that water vapor is less dense (lighter) than oxygen is explained. An atom of oxygen weighs approximately sixteen times as much as an atom of hydrogen, we now know, which means that n molecules of H_2O weigh only $18/32$ as much (approximately) as n molecules of O_2.

Avogadro's proposals are now accepted as essentially correct. They were not, however, widely accepted among the great Italian's contemporaries. Nearly fifty years passed before another Italian scientist, Cannizzaro, presented to the scientific world his *Sketch of a Course in Chemical Philosophy*, wherein he made a very convincing restatement of Avogadro's arguments and conclusions, buttressing them with a wealth of data accumulated since Avogadro's day. The way was thus opened to further developments of atomic-molecular theory and to experiments leading, in our day, toward the harnessing of atomic energy and the conquest of outer space.

* Avogadro assumed H_4O_2 to be a transitory or intermediate and unstable molecule which almost instantaneously divided into two molecules of H_2O.

CHAPTER 3

Physical Causes of
Unusual Properties

What IS "Cause-and-Effect"?

In the first chapter of this book we pointed out several of the peculiarities of water as a physical entity or chemical compound, peculiarities justifying our assertion that water as viewed by the physical chemist is a most unusual substance. We propose in the present chapter to consider the causes of these peculiarities as science has thus far discerned them. Before we do so, however, we should perhaps clarify as much as possible what is meant by "cause" and "effect" in the language of science, for few words are more confused and confusing in their meaning than these.[1]

When we say in science that A is the cause of B or that B occurs (or exists) because of A, we do not mean that A produces B, or generates it, or creates it in the sense of the Creation in Genesis. In these latter concepts are elements of force, or motive power, of purpose—elements wholly absent from the "causality" of science. What the scientist means by "A causes B" is simply that A and B are observed in

[1] In his *An Approach to Modern Physics* (Doubleday Anchor, 1957), E. N. da C. Andrade points out (page 247) that the word represented by "cause" has sixty-four meanings in the writings of Plato and forty-eight in those of Aristotle.

nature, under prescribed conditions, to be always conjoined in a certain spatial and temporal sequence, so that if A occurs or exists, B does or will also. Of course, a scientist may describe his experiment as an attempt to find out why such-and-such a thing happens as it does, and may conclude (if his experiment succeeds) that it happens because of something else; and this "something else" always turns out to be simply an extension of the scientist's initial knowledge of what happens and how it happens. The scientist sees cause and effect as ultimately continuous with one another, each being but an aspect of, or abstraction from, a single reality or process.

To illustrate:

Having observed a freely falling drop of water assuming, as always, a spherical shape, you ask the scientist, "Why?" He answers, "Because water has a high surface tension." And at once you see that the scientist's assigned cause of the phenomenon you observed is but an enlargement of your initial observation, extending the knowledge it presented to you. What you observed was simply surface tension in action; the "effect" (the sphericality of the drop) was but an aspect or manifestation of its "cause" (surface tension). The scientist says: falling drops of a liquid having high surface tension become spherical. The scientist might even go on to say that falling drops "obey" the natural law he implies, but if he does so he means something very different from the kind of obedience you manifest when you drive your car according to the traffic rules. The traffic rules actually govern, through persuasive and coercive power, the flow of traffic and the behavior of individuals, but natural or scientific laws merely describe in a logically coherent form what we consistently observe in nature. The natural order which scientific law seeks to describe does not cause anything in nature; the order simply *is,* and everything that naturally occurs is a part of it.

So it will be with our attempts to answer in this chapter the question of why water has so abnormally high a surface tension, why it is so remarkable in its heat relations, why it is able to act as an almost universal solvent, why it has a unique ability to "wet" other substances. Each answer must be simply a description of what the peculiarity manifests and how the manifestation occurs; it must ignore as irrelevant the kind of "why" that requires to be answered in terms of intention or purpose.

Atoms in Nineteenth-Century Chemistry

We have told of the development of atomic theory in the eighteenth and early nineteenth centuries, a development of which the continuing discovery of water's nature was part and parcel. We closed the preceding chapter with Avogadro's conception of the molecule, a combination of two or more atoms, as the constituent "particle" of chemical substances. But we stressed that this was by no means the end of the evolution of atomic-molecular theory. On the contrary, it was the merest beginning. We have now to trace, very briefly and sketchily, this later evolution, since some understanding of its results is essential to our present-day conception of water's molecular structure and consequent behavior.

The first step in this evolutionary development was the establishment of the atomic weights of the various elements, a step which might at first glance seem to you difficult to the point of impossibility. Atoms, even as Dalton conceived them, are infinitesimal, and no one in the nineteenth century could even guess how many might exist in any given volume. How, then, could atoms be weighed? Of course they couldn't be, one by one. Three factors operated, however, to make the establishment of atomic weights a fairly simple matter. In the first place, weight, like size, is a relative property; it is in fact a quantitative relationship between different things, one that is determined by measuring those things against a single standard scale, and we may choose as our standard of measurement whatever we please so long as we hold the chosen unit rigorously constant. In the second place, each chemical element consists by definition of atoms that, equal to one another in weight, differ in weight from the atoms of any other element. (We shall not consider isotopes here.) And in the third place, the elements form chemical combinations (when they combine at all) in certain invariable proportions. It was therefore possible not only to assign each atom a position on a scale ranging from the lightest to the heaviest of them (this might be done simply by weighing equivalent volumes, if one could assume that equal volumes contained equal numbers of atoms), but also to give a numerical value to each position, a value worked out into smaller and smaller fractions as the methods of quantitative chemistry were refined. This value was the element's atomic weight.

For instance, we know that 1 weight unit of hydrogen (a gram, an ounce, or any other such unit) burns or oxidizes to produce 18 units of water, and that there are twice as many hydrogen atoms as there are oxygen atoms in any given quantity of water, since the chemical formula for water is H_2O. If we assign to the hydrogen atom a weight of 1, therefore, the atomic weight of oxygen becomes 16—and having determined oxygen's weight in this way, we can go on to determine the weights of elements that combine with it. There are very many that do. Copper, for example, combines with oxygen in the weight ratio of 127.2 to 16 to form 143.2 units of copper oxide

TYPE →	R_2O	RO	R_2O_3	RH_4 RO_2	RH_3 R_2O_5	RH_2 RO_3	RH R_2O_7	RO_4
GROUP →	I	II	III	IV	V	VI	VII	VIII
SERIES 1	H=1 HYDROGEN							
SERIES 2	Li=7 LITHIUM	Be=9.4 BERYLLIUM	B=11 BORON	C=12 CARBON	N=14 NITROGEN	O=16 OXYGEN	F=19 FLUORINE	
SERIES 3	Na=23 SODIUM	Mg=24 MAGNESIUM	Al=27.3 ALUMINUM	Si=28 SILICON	P=31 PHOSPHORUS	S=32 SULFUR	Cl=35.5 CHLORINE	
SERIES 4	K=39 POTASSIUM	Ca=40 CALCIUM	—=44	Ti=48 TITANIUM	V=51 VANADIUM	Cr=52 CHROMIUM	Mn=55 MANGANESE	Fe=56 IRON, Co=59 COBALT, Ni=59 NICKEL, Cu=63 COPPER
SERIES 5	(Cu=63) COPPER	Zn=65 ZINC	—=68	—=72	As=75 ARSENIC	Se=78 SELENIUM	Br=80 BROMINE	
SERIES 6	Rb=85 RUBIDIUM	Sr=87 STRONTIUM	?Y=88 YTTRIUM	Zr=90 ZIRCONIUM	Nb=94 NIOBIUM	Mo=96 MOLYBDENUM	—=100	Ru=103 RUTHENIUM, Rh=104 RHODIUM, Pd=106 PALLADIUM, Ag=108 SILVER
SERIES 7	(Ag=108) SILVER	Cd=112 CADMIUM	In=113 INDIUM	Sn=118 TIN	Sb=122 ANTIMONY	Te=125 TELLURIUM	I=127 IODINE	—
SERIES 8	Cs=133 CESIUM	Ba=137 BARIUM	?Di=138	?Ce=140 CERIUM	—	—	—	—
SERIES 9	—	—	—	—	—	—	—	
SERIES 10	—	—	?Er=178 ERBIUM	?La=180 LANTHANUM	Ta=182 TANTALUM	W=184 WOLFRAM	—	Os=195 OSMIUM, Ir=197 IRIDIUM, Pt=198 PLATINUM, Au=199 GOLD
SERIES 11	(Au=199) GOLD	Hg=200 MERCURY	Tl=204 THALLIUM	Pb=207 LEAD	Bi=208 BISMUTH	—	—	
SERIES 12	—	—	—	Th=231 THORIUM	—	U=240 URANIUM	—	—

FIG. 8. The periodic table, published in this form in 1872 by the great Russian chemist Dimitri Ivanovich Mendeleyev, grouped the elements by families and in order of atomic weights to form an arrangement that showed the periodicity of the elements' chemical properties. It was Mendeleyev's bold contribution to leave the vacancies you see in the table and to predict that then unknown elements would be discovered to fill the vacancies.

TYPE →	R_2O RH	RO RH_2	R_2O_3	RO_2	R_2O_5	RO_3	R_2O_7	RO_4			R_2O	RO	R_2O_3	RO_2 RH_4	R_2O_5 H_3R	RO_3 H_2R	R_2O_7 HR	VIIIA INERT GASES
GROUP →	IA	IIA	IIIB	IVB	VB	VIB	VIIB	VIIIB			IB	IIB	IIIA	IVA	VA	VIA	VIIA	VIIA
PERIOD 1	1 H HYDROGEN 1.0080																	2 He HELIUM 4.003
PERIOD 2	3 Li LITHIUM 6.940	4 Be BERYLLIUM 9.013											5 B BORON 10.82	6 C CARBON 12.011	7 N NITROGEN 14.008	8 O OXYGEN 16.000	9 F FLUORINE 19.000	10 Ne NEON 20.183
PERIOD 3	11 Na SODIUM 22.991	12 Mg MAGNESIUM 24.32											13 Al ALUMINUM 26.98	14 Si SILICON 28.09	15 P PHOSPHORUS 30.975	16 S SULFUR 32.066	17 Cl CHLORINE 35.457	18 A ARGON 39.944
PERIOD 4	19 K POTASSIUM 39.100	20 Ca CALCIUM 40.08	21 Sc SCANDIUM 45.10	22 Ti TITANIUM 47.90	23 V VANADIUM 50.95	24 Cr CHROMIUM 52.01	25 Mn MANGANESE 54.94	26 Fe IRON 55.85	27 Co COBALT 58.94	28 Ni NICKEL 58.71	29 Cu COPPER 63.54	30 Zn ZINC 65.38	31 Ga GALLIUM 69.72	32 Ge GERMANIUM 72.60	33 As ARSENIC 74.91	34 Se SELENIUM 78.96	35 Br BROMINE 79.916	36 Kr KRYPTON 83.80
PERIOD 5	37 Rb RUBIDIUM 85.48	38 Sr STRONTIUM 87.63	39 Y YTTRIUM 88.92	40 Zr ZIRCONIUM 91.22	41 Nb NIOBIUM 92.91	42 Mo MOLYBDENUM 95.95	43 Tc TECHNETIUM (99)	44 Ru RUTHENIUM 101.1	45 Rh RHODIUM 102.91	46 Pd PALLADIUM 106.7	47 Ag SILVER 107.880	48 Cd CADMIUM 112.41	49 In INDIUM 114.76	50 Sn TIN 118.70	51 Sb ANTIMONY 121.76	52 Te TELLURIUM 127.61	53 I IODINE 126.91	54 Xe XENON 131.3
PERIOD 6	55 Cs CESIUM 132.91	56 Ba BARIUM 137.36	57–71*	72 Hf HAFNIUM 178.58	73 Ta TANTALUM 180.95	74 W WOLFRAM 183.86	75 Re RHENIUM 186.22	76 Os OSMIUM 190.2	77 Ir IRIDIUM 192.2	78 Pt PLATINUM 195.23	79 Au GOLD 197.0	80 Hg MERCURY 200.61	81 Tl THALLIUM 204.39	82 Pb LEAD 207.21	83 Bi BISMUTH 209.00	84 Po POLONIUM 210–	85 At ASTATINE (211–)	86 Rn RADON 222–
PERIOD 7	87 Fr FRANCIUM (223)	88 Ra RADIUM 226.05	89–93**															

RARE EARTH ELEMENTS

*LANTHANIDE SERIES

57 La LANTHANUM 138.92	58* Ce CERIUM 140.13	59 Pr PRASEODYMIUM 140.92	60 Nd NEODYMIUM 144.27	61 Pm PROMETHIUM (145)	62 Sm SAMARIUM 150.35	63 Eu EUROPIUM 152.0	64 Gd GADOLINIUM 156.9	65 Tb TERBIUM 158.93	66 Dy DYSPROSIUM 162.51	67 Ho HOLMIUM 164.94	68 Er ERBIUM 167.27	69 Tm THULIUM 168.94	70 Yb YTTERBIUM 173.04	71 Lu LUTETIUM 174.99

**ACTINIDE SERIES

89 Ac ACTINIUM 227.0	90 Th THORIUM 232.05	91 Pa PROTACTINIUM 231–	92 U URANIUM 238.07	93 Np NEPTUNIUM (237)	94 Pu PLUTONIUM (242)	95 Am AMERICIUM (243)	96 Cm CURIUM (245)	97 Bk BERKELIUM (249)	98 Cf CALIFORNIUM (249)	99 E EINSTEINIUM (252)	100 Fm FERMIUM (252)	101 Mv MENDELEVIUM (256)	102 No NOBELIUM (254)	103? —

LIGHT METALS   HEAVY METALS   NONMETALS   INERT GASES

FIG. 9.   The modern periodic table differs from Mendeleev's in ordering the elements according to atomic number rather than atomic weights. (The atomic number of an element is the number of protons in its nucleus.) This modern table includes, of course, the natural elements discovered since Mendeleev's day and the elements artificially produced since World War II.

(Cu_2O); this means that the copper atom weighs 63.6 times as much as the hydrogen atom and has by that token an atomic weight of 63.6. From this we can determine by the same procedure the atomic weights of elements with which copper combines. Take sulfur, of which 32.1 weight units combine with 63.6 units of copper to produce 95.7 units of copper sulfide (Cu_2S). This indicates that the sulfur atom has the weight of 32.1 hydrogen atoms—an atomic weight, in other words, of 32.1 Thus, through many thousands of laboratory experiments in quantitative analysis, the combining weights of all known elements were determined and, from these, the atomic weight of each element was deduced.[2]

The next step was accomplished in large part by a Russian named Dimitri Mendeleyev (or Mendeleeff). In 1869 he published his epoch-making discovery[3] that the elements when arranged in the order of increasing atomic weights exhibit a sharply defined *periodicity* of properties or behavior. The lightest element, hydrogen, did not fit into the scheme as Mendeleyev discerned it, but beginning with the next-heavier of the then known elements, lithium, he found that similar chemical properties occurred in

[2] We must add that several decades after atomic weights had been assigned in the manner here described, it was found through very precise quantitative analyses of water that the actual ratio of atomic weights for oxygen and hydrogen varied by nearly 1 per cent from 1:16. The true ratio is 1.008:16. It was thereupon decided that oxygen, in terms of whose atomic weight of 16 most other atomic weights had been determined, should replace hydrogen as the base of all atomic weights. By this decision the necessity to change every element's atomic weight was avoided and only hydrogen's had to be changed, from 1 to 1.008.

[3] Actually Mendeleyev's work was the culmination of a process of discovery in which a German, J. W. Döbereiner, a Frenchman, A. E. B. de Chancourtois, and an Englishman, J. A. R. Newlands, played leading roles. They laid the stepping-stones on which the Russian mounted to his triumph.

every seventh element as one went down the list. Thus lithium is a metal whose oxide dissolves in water to form a strong alkali. Seven elements down the list is sodium, also a metal whose dissolved oxide produces an alkali. Seven elements down from sodium is potassium, yet another alkali-producing metal. Moreover, the elements immediately adjacent (Fig. 8) exhibit similar properties. Beryllium is next to lithium in weight, magnesium is next to sodium, calcium is next to potassium—and these elements obviously belong together in the same way as do the first three we named, for they have many chemical characteristics in common. As a matter of fact, if one began with lithium and placed the first twenty-one of the elements known to Mendeleyev in horizontal periods of seven, stacking these rows of seven atop each other, one formed seven vertical columns each of three elements whose chemical natures were closely related. Things became somewhat more difficult as one came to the heavier elements. Here Mendeleyev found it necessary to alternate periods of ten with periods of seven. But in the end he was so convinced of the objective truth of periodicity that he boldly left gaps in his table to indicate six as yet unknown elements, whose general properties he described. The quick discovery of three of these elements (the other three have since been found) was a great triumph for Mendeleyev.[4] And the triumph has re-

[4] One of the unknown elements was called "ekasilicon" by Mendeleyev when, in 1871, he predicted its discovery and described its properties. Isolated in 1886 and named germanium, the element's actual properties compared with those predicted for it are in part as follows:

mained valid as later discoveries, while modifying Mendeleyev's original table (Fig. 9), have provided further confirmation of the essential truth of his concept. For instance, the discovery of the inert gases resulted in a lengthening of the periods by one element, but once the first two (helium and argon) had been found and placed at the ends of the first and third periods, the discovery of the other four (neon, krypton, xenon, and radon) could be confidently predicted and facilitated by application of the "periodic law."

The third step in the evolution of atomic-molecular theory broke down once and for all the barrier which had theretofore separated chemistry from physics. This step was a radical revision of all earlier ideas of what an atom *is*—in other words, of its structure and nature and behavior.

Until the closing years of the nineteenth century, chemists held to the ancient notion that an atom (the word comes from the Greek for "indivisible") was an infinitely small pebble-like particle "so very hard," to repeat Newton's words, "as never to wear or break to pieces." Every element was made up of a distinctive kind of atom; the atoms of no two elements agreed precisely in size, for one thing; and the extreme solidity or hardness of these ultimate particles —their indestructible integrity—precluded the possibility of any such transmutation of elements as the medieval alchemist had sought to achieve. No atom

---

Ekasilicon

Atomic wt. 72, density 5.5

Oxide EsO_2, density 4.7

Chloride $EsCl_4$, liquid boiling slightly below 100° C., density 1.9

Sulfide EsS_2 insoluble in water but soluble in ammonium sulfide

Germanium

Atomic wt. 72.6, density 5.46

Oxide GeO_2, density 4.7

Chloride $GeCl_4$, liquid boiling at 86° C., density 1.887

Sulfide GeS_2 insoluble in water but readily soluble in ammonium sulfide

could be split or chipped or in any way changed in its shape and composition; it must remain forever what it had been from the moment of creation. This concept of the atom seemed to the chemist abundantly confirmed by his laboratory experiments. The laws whereby the elements formed chemical combinations in rigidly prescribed proportions by weight and volume, the general law of the conservation of matter, Mendeleyev's periodic chart of the atoms—all these seemed to indicate the kind of ultimate particle Newton and Dalton had described.

But the atomic concept which seemed so clear and was so useful to the chemist carried no such recommendation to the nineteenth-century physicist. It settled no question for him as he pursued his studies of matter and energy—of mechanics, heat, light, electricity, and so on. Instead, it raised questions he couldn't answer. He readily agreed that matter must be made up of tiny particles, since this accorded with his observations of the physical properties of liquids and gases and solids. He even (generally) called these particles "molecules." But that molecules were combinations of two or more atoms, as chemistry asserted, was to the physicist incomprehensible and inexplicable by the well-established laws of his science. Nor could he invent new laws to explain this behavior on the basis of existing knowledge in his field. What brought these infinitesimal particles together in unit combinations? What forces *could* bind them together if they were indeed as hard, as impenetrable and unchangeable, as chemistry alleged? It must be some force wholly outside the atoms themselves. And why was atomic weight of such importance, determining (it seemed) all kinds of chemical behavior? Such questions caused many a physicist to conclude that the atom was a mere fiction, useful to chemistry, useless to physics. Some chemists, too, dismissing the atom as a useless concept, confined their theorizing to combining weights.

As a matter of fact, the physicist could find no place for chemical atoms in his scheme of things until, paradoxically, such atoms had ceased to exist. At least they ceased to exist in any form that Dalton would have recognized.

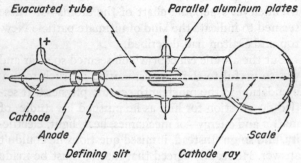

FIG. 10. *The cathode-ray tube, of the type used by J. J. Thomson in his discovery of the electron, is schematically illustrated here. The tube is a sealed glass bulb evacuated of air. When its cathode is attached to the negative pole of a battery or other source of current and its anode to the positive pole, electrons flow from the cathode to the anode. Passing through the slit in the anode and the defining slit, they form a ray (dotted path). When voltages are applied across the parallel plates, the ray is deflected, and the deflections can be read on the scale.*

The initially puzzling clues that were to lead eventually to a wholly different concept of matter were found, not in the test tubes of Dalton's successors, but in the cathode-ray tube of the physicists. This device (Fig. 10) is nothing more than a sealed glass receptacle from which the air has been pumped and through which an electric current is passed. In early 1896, while studying the curious fluorescent properties of such a tube, a German named Wilhelm Roentgen discovered X rays. He had no notion what they might be (hence his name for them), but it was obvious that his finding was important and that previous theory did not account for the phenomenon.

In a matter of weeks Henri Becquerel, a French chemist, was engaged in a research project suggested by Roentgen's discovery. Quite by accident, of which he took immediate and discerning advantage, he discovered that uranium ore emitted mysterious penetrating rays different from Roentgen's X rays.

Meanwhile, the great British physicist J. J. Thomson (1856–1940) was busying himself with a study of the electrical discharge within the cathode tube itself. In 1897, after a long series of experiments and calculations, he was able to announce with confidence that the electricity passing through the tube was negative, was carried in discrete amounts and *by individual particles*. He could calculate the ratio of the mass of the particle to its charge and had learned that this ratio was only $\frac{1}{1000}$ of the known ratio of the positive hydrogen ion to its charge. The conclusion was inescapable. The atom no longer was indivisible. The negative-charge carrier, the *electron*, was a constituent of atoms.

Research prompted by Becquerel's discovery of penetrating rays from uranium produced new findings. Three years after his announcement Pierre and Marie Curie, in Paris, having completed a staggering program of analysis, announced the discovery of two new elements, polonium and radium, the latter of which emitted penetrating rays at a million times the rate of uranium ore.

These discoveries meant the end of the old concept of the atom as a "solid, massy" particle which had persisted and must persist unaltered through all time. Radioactivity, as the emission of rays was called, meant that the transmutation of elements, far from being impossible, is going on all the time—a natural spontaneous occurrence among the heaviest elements. A radioactive element is continuously breaking down to make, sometimes, "isotopes" or different forms of itself, forms having lower atomic weights but retaining the same chemical properties; and, sometimes, a different element altogether, one of distinctly lower atomic weight and markedly different chemical behavior. The newly made element may then continue the process, disintegrating through a series of isotopes into a different, lighter element. Indeed, it was found that naturally radioactive substances can be placed in one of three so-called "radioactive series" —the *uranium series*, of which both radium and polonium are a part; the *thorium series*; and the *actinium series*. (There also is a fourth, an artificially created *neptunium series*, discovered in the preparation of the first atomic bomb.) Each of these series ends in a non-radioactive isotope of lead, one distinguishable from ordinary lead only by its appreciably different atomic weight.

Atoms in Twentieth-Century Physics

As we have said, the discovery of the electron and of transmutation meant the destruction forever of the old concept of the atom. But we must at once add that the process by which the old was destroyed led directly, as always happens in science, to the creation of the new. Studies of the mysterious rays emitted by radioactive materials were at once initiated. These soon opened up the hitherto unsuspected country of atomic or (to be exact) nuclear physics, with all its grandeurs and terrors for modern men. And though it is a country which need not be penetrated at all deeply by us in this book, we must cross its border if we are to appreciate water's peculiar properties.

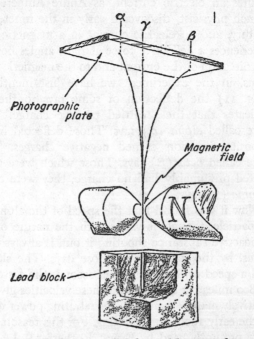

FIG. 11.   *Deflections of alpha and beta rays by magnetic fields were measured with apparatus like this in the early experiments with radioactivity. Gamma rays, as the illustration shows, passed through the field without deflection.*

The emitted rays of radioactivity were quickly shown to be of different kinds, for when they were aimed at a photographic plate across a strong magnetic field they separated into three streams, producing on the plate three distinct lines of exposure. Perhaps a word of explanation is needed here. As you know, there are two kinds of electric charge, called (originally by Benjamin Franklin) *positive* and *nega-*

tive; like charges repel one another, unlike charges attract one another. When a charge moves, it constitutes an electric current, as André Ampère, the French physicist, discovered early in the nineteenth century, and an electric current in a magnetic field experiences a deflective force at right angles both to the direction of the current and to the magnetic field. Thus, in the experiment we have just mentioned (Fig. 11) the deflection of some rays to the left indicates that these carried positive charge. They were called *alpha* (α) rays. Those deflected in the opposite direction carried negative charges. They were called *beta* (β) rays. Those which were undeflected presumably had no charge; they were called *gamma* (γ) rays.

Now it was found that the speed of the alpha ray or particle, though it varies with the nature of the radioactive substance shooting it out, is always enormous, by the standards of those days. The slowest had a speed of 8800 miles per second, the fastest of 12,800 miles per second, and these velocities give the relatively massive particles a penetrating power which in the early 1900s was amazing. For this reason, they were promptly used by Ernest Rutherford, the English physicist, to bombard extremely thin sheets of metal (Fig. 12) in as important a single experiment as has ever been conducted in the whole history of science. He found that nearly all the α-particles shot through the metal with little or no deflection, as they were expected to—but some did not. A very few of them were deflected at wide angles from a straight course; now and then one of them actually came straight back toward its source! "It was almost as incredible as if you had fired a 15-inch shell at a piece of tissue paper and it had come back and hit you," Rutherford said later. He at once inferred that the widely deflected alpha rays had run into positively charged particles of at least equivalent mass. When he repeated the experiment, using other substances for targets, he was convinced, as was the scientific world, that every atom has a center of positive electrical charge that is concentrated in a small space which also includes a major fraction of its total mass (meaning weight, not size). From this experiment Rutherford postulated the existence of the *nucleus* of the atom, whose positive charge balanced in an electric field a number of negatively charged particles (as they were then conceived to be) called *electrons*.

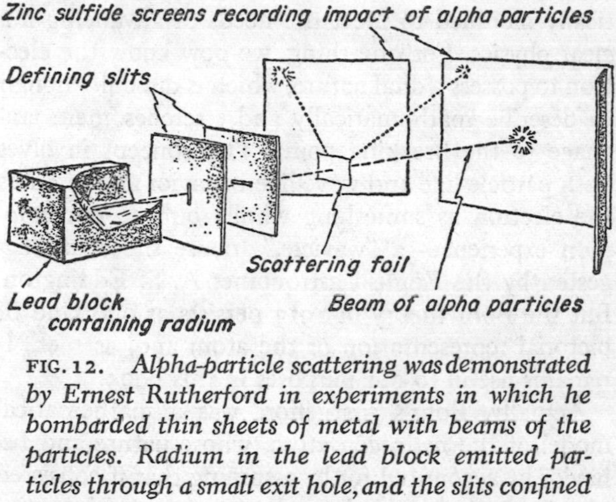

FIG. 12. *Alpha-particle scattering was demonstrated by Ernest Rutherford in experiments in which he bombarded thin sheets of metal with beams of the particles. Radium in the lead block emitted particles through a small exit hole, and the slits confined the emission to a beam, which passed through the foil and struck the zinc sulfide screens.*

It was soon apparent that the nucleus is the source of the rays emitted in radioactivity, that radioactivity is a process of nuclear disintegration. Beta rays are simply electrons, each carrying one unit of negative charge. Alpha rays turned out to be helium nuclei stripped of their electrons, as Rutherford and an associate found when they fired α-particles through a thin sheet of glass into an escape-proof chamber. This chamber gradually filled with helium gas, indicating that the α-particles had attached electrons to themselves as they passed through the glass sheet. The α-particle consists of two protons, each carrying one unit of positive electric charge. As for the gamma ray, it was found to be similar to the X ray but of very high frequency.

Shortly thereafter the Danish physicist Niels Bohr developed a theory of the atom as a kind of infinitesimal solar system with the nucleus as sun and the circling electrons as planets. It is a theory since drastically modified to meet the needs of advancing nuclear physics. For one thing, we now know the electron to possess a dual nature, which is difficult enough to describe mathematically and stretches mere language to the breaking point. The concept involves both particle-like and wave-like behavior and pictures the electron as something wholly outside our common experience—a "wavicle," to use the term suggested by the English astronomer A. S. Eddington. But the Bohr theory of 1913 persists as one kind of pictorial representation of the atom and, as such, it remains useful to our purposes in this book.

Actually, Bohr's first effort was a mathematical model of the hydrogen atom, whose nature and behavior he accounted for by assuming that it consisted of a single positively charged *proton* circled by a single negatively charged electron, the latter having about $\frac{1}{2000}$ the mass of the former. When Bohr went on to encompass the heavier atoms in his theory, he encountered grave difficulties, but in the end he found it useful to assume that the number of protons or units of positive charge in the nucleus (which is the same as the number of electrons in the neutral atom's outer shells) coincided with the *atomic number* of the element—with its position, in other words,

PLATE I. Floating steel illustrates the magnitude of the surface tension of water. The perforated piece of steel in this picture is one thirty-second of an inch thick and weighs 2.5 grams. The hemispheres of water rising through the perforations are another effect of surface tension. *Educational Services Incorporated, George Daffin Cope.*

PLATE II. The hexagonal structure of snow crystals, presumably determined by the tetrahedral molecular structure of ice, is shown in these microphotographs, striking examples of the symmetrical beauty of some of nature's forms.

Courtesy USWB—W. A. Bentley.

on the list from lightest to heaviest. Thus hydrogen, the lightest element, has an atomic number of 1, which is taken to mean that its nucleus contains a single proton. Helium, the next-to-lightest element, has by that token an atomic number of 2, indicating that its nucleus contains two protons. The lithium nucleus has three (atomic number 3), the beryllium four, the boron five, and so on down the list. The uranium atom has 92 protons in its nucleus and, therefore, 92 electrons orbiting or vibrating around the nucleus.

We must add that protons, though the number of them in the nucleus is deemed identical with the atomic number, do not make up the whole mass of the nucleus. If protons were the only nuclear constituent, there could be no such things as isotopes (those atoms of the same element having different weights), for in that case any reduction in weight would inevitably mean a reduction in the nuclear charge; this in turn would mean a change in electronic structure and therefore in chemical behavior. But isotopes *do* exist; as a matter of fact, the accepted atomic weight of an element has recently been shown to be an average of the weights of its naturally occurring isotopes, the latter occurring in whole numbers only. Hence nuclear particles other than protons exist.

Nor is this the only evidence of their existence. Far from it. Nuclear research, whose discoveries succeed one another with bewildering rapidity, has shown the nuclear structure to be complex indeed. One major tool of this research is itself a nuclear particle called the *neutron*. Rutherford postulated the existence of the neutron around 1920, and his associate James Chadwick unmistakably detected it in 1932. As the name suggests, the neutron has no electric charge, but it does have weight and accounts for no small proportion of the total mass of most elements. The neutron is uniquely capable of probing atomic secrets. Having no charge, it is not deflected, as charged particles would be, when it passes through electromagnetic fields. Equally indifferent to the charges of protons and electrons—attracted by neither, repelled by neither—the neutron has extraordinary penetrating power. In various ways it can be speeded up or slowed down to carry out particular atomic explorations, and it is the principal tool for inducing artificial radioactivity and, on occasion, inciting those chain reactions which, by releasing undreamed-of energies, hold so much of threat and promise for the future.

We should further add (since the immediately preceding paragraphs may well have raised questions in your mind) that the Coulomb law of electrical attraction and repulsion, which accurately describes the actions of the atom as a whole, and the actions of charged particles emitted from radioactive nuclei, is inadequate to describe the actions of particles—or *nucleons*, as they are called—within the stable nucleus. Indeed, this law, operating without qualification, or in the absence of any other force, would make it impossible for a nucleus to contain more than one proton; two protons must violently repel one another. The fact that they do not—that, on the contrary, as many as one-hundred-odd protons may coexist in an extremely compact nucleus—is accounted for by what are called *nuclear forces*. These nuclear forces operate only at very short range, providing the "glue" holding nucleons together, or the binding energy which must be overcome if the nucleus is to be split, and they vary inversely with the size of the nucleus. In a nucleus of moderate size (atomic number 50 or thereabouts) the binding energy amounts to some 8.8 million electron volts per nucleon, but the energy decreases to about 7.6 million electron volts per nucleon in a nucleus of large size (atomic number of around 240). Why? Evidently the Coulomb repulsion, overwhelmed by nuclear forces within the super-dense nucleus, nevertheless becomes increasingly effectual as the distance increases between the most widely separated nucleons. The difference of 1.2 million electron volts of binding energy, as between moderate-sized and large-sized nuclei, may therefore be said to represent the reducing effect of the Coulomb repulsion upon the nuclear forces. This in turn suggests that at a certain point the two opposing forces will be precisely balanced and that upon or through this point, being determined by it, will lie the boundary or surface of the largest possible stable nucleus.

In any case, the nuclear forces acting upon the nucleons produce a nuclear surface effect akin to that determining the sphericality of a water drop. Since every nucleon in the interior is pulled equally in all directions while the nucleons on the surface are pulled inward much more strongly than they are outward, a surface-tension effect is created. This has made it possible to discuss the nucleus as if it behaved like a droplet of water (the so-called liquid-drop model of the nucleus), and the model helps physicists to visualize the processes of nuclear fusion and fission.

Niels Bohr first made the analogy in 1936, and subsequent research has confirmed its usefulness. When the nucleus is struck by a ray or particle of sufficient energy to penetrate its surface, it is affected much as a drop of water would be if struck by a tiny bullet. It may either "evaporate" or "shake to pieces," depending upon its size and the energy of the "bullet." The energy is shared by the nucleons, which are thereby "heated up," and if the "thermal agitation" is great enough the nucleons will fly apart as water molecules do when sufficient heat is applied to them.

Since nuclear volume is directly proportional to nuclear weight, the heaviest nuclei behave like large drops of water. Struck by a "bullet," they vibrate and break into two or more spherical drops.[5]

But what about the electron?—you may well ask. What keeps it with its negative charge from being drawn to the positively charged nucleus? Its speed does, according to the Rutherford-Bohr conception we have been describing. Actually, by this conception, the electron is continually falling toward the nucleus, just as the moon is continually falling toward the earth, and it is the forward motion of the electron (like the forward movement of the moon) that combines with the inward fall to determine the orbit. In the case of the electron, though, the necessary speed is tremendous, amounting to several hundreds of miles per second, which means that the electron (by this view) orbits the nucleus several thousand million million times a second!

The New Physics and the Periodic Table

The picture of the atom which emerges from all this (though it is, we repeat, a highly simplified one not to be taken as an accurate representation) is very strange to common sense. In the first place, we must repeat and emphasize that an atomic particle—an electron, or nucleus, or component of the latter—is not a solid, pebble-like structure, but is, instead, a center of electrical force. When we speak of its size, therefore, we are referring, not to a solidly filled space such as is occupied (to our common-sense vision) by an orange, but instead to the space normally dominated by the center of electrical force.

[5] E. N. da C. Andrade discusses all this in more detail on pages 211–19 of his *An Approach to Modern Physics*, which is heartily recommended to you.

From subtle and indirect measurements of the dimensions of atoms we know that if we magnified (for example) a neutral oxygen atom a million million times we should find that its nucleus, consisting of eight protons and eight neutrons (atomic weight 16), was in effect a sphere about the size of a pea. Around it would be moving eight electrons (oxygen's atomic number is 8), the farthest about a hundred yards away and each of them about the size of a large orange. If we assigned to each electron the weight of an orange, however, we should find that the pea-sized nucleus had a relative weight of one ton, for its density is some 500 million million times that of a water drop! Thus the oxygen atom, like all other atoms (and like our solar system) is mostly empty space. As J. W. N. Sullivan has said, in his *The Limitations of Science* (Mentor), "If all the atoms of a man's body were so condensed as to leave no unfilled space, the man's body would become a barely visible speck."

This is strange enough to our ordinary view of things, and the strangeness is compounded in the revisions of Bohr's original conception of the atom. It has been found, for instance, that the single electron of the hydrogen atom does not revolve in a fixed circular orbit around the proton, as Bohr assumed it did. Instead it moves in a rather random fashion, sometimes coming very near the nucleus and sometimes shooting relatively far away from it; its motion for the most part is either toward or away from the center. So great is the speed with which it darts in and out, and over and around, that it in effect occupies a globular space with a radius of about 1 Å (for Ångstrom), which is a hundred millionth of a centimeter. "Thus we can speak of the free hydrogen atom as having a heavy nucleus at the center of a mushy sphere defined by the space filled by the fast-moving electron in its motion about the nucleus," writes

Linus Pauling. "This mushy sphere is about 2 Å in diameter." All the same, the hydrogen electron does have a most probable distance from the nucleus—that is, a distance it is most likely to be from the nucleus at any instant—and this is precisely the one calculated by Bohr as the assumed fixed orbit, a distance of 0.529 Å from the nucleus.

In terms of probability the same is true of the electrons of other, heavier atoms. It is common to speak of the atom as an electron cloud centered on the nucleus. The number of electrons in the cloud is determined by the number of positive charges (protons) in the nucleus, there being precisely as many of the former as there are of the latter in a neutral atom. It is absolutely impossible to make a precise determination of the position of an electron at any instant, since the effort to do so inevitably disturbs the electron's behavior in unpredictable ways, but it *is* possible to determine the most probable position of one —to determine, in other words, the region within which the electron at any given instant is most likely to be found. Such regions may be pictured as forming concentric spheres or shells around the nucleus, and it is normally the electrons in the outer shell—the shell farthest removed from the nucleus—that are involved in chemical reactions.

The atom's chemical properties, then, are determined by the nucleus, whose protons account for the positive charge and, with neutrons (though these have little effect on chemistry), for practically the whole of the atomic weight. The extremely lightweight electrons, however, are the particles actively involved in chemical exchanges or reactions.

If the neutral atom loses electrons from its outer shell, it becomes a positive ion with a charge equivalent to the number of electrons lost; if its outer shell gains electrons it becomes a negative ion with a charge equivalent to the number of electrons gained; and when two atoms combine to form molecules, whether molecules of the same element, as in H_2, or of a compound, as in H_2O, the operation is generally one of sharing or exchanging outer electrons.

Moreover (and we now approach the heart of the matter which concerns us in this chapter), *the tendency of the outer shell to gain or lose electrons varies among the elements according to certain definite rules*. The scientific "why" of this, as elaborated in quantum theory with its exclusion principle, is impossible to express in non-mathematical language without using up more space than we can give to it here, but the rule itself as manifested in the periodic chart of the elements (Mendeleyev's chart, you'll remember) is simple enough.

Let's look again at this chart, in the light of our new knowledge:

The first period on it contains only two elements, hydrogen and helium, the former with a single electron, according to our theory, and the latter with two. Hydrogen we know as a chemically active gas, eager to enter into chemical combinations, whereas helium is a chemically inert gas, stubbornly resistant to chemical combinations. The second period on the chart contains eight elements, beginning with lithium (atomic number 3, meaning three electrons) and ending with neon (10). The former is a soft alkali metal, entering readily into chemical compounds; the latter is an inert gas like helium. The third period of eight elements also begins with a soft alkali metal, sodium (11), and ends with an inert gas, argon (18). The fourth period is longer, running from potassium (19) to krypton (36), but, like the preceding ones, it begins with a soft alkali metal and ends with an inert gas. Inserted in the middle of this period is a new class of elements, having properties unlike those of any preceding element but very like those of the middle class of the next period, a period which also contains eighteen elements. This fifth period repeats the earlier pattern in that it opens with rubidium (37), a soft alkali metal, and ends with the inert gas xenon (54). The sixth period is very long and complex. Beginning with cesium (55), it ends with radon (86); it contains, in other words, thirty-two elements, of which the last is a disintegration product of radium's radioactivity. But it is similar to earlier periods to the extent that cesium is an alkali metal and radon behaves as an inert gas. As for the elements in the seventh and last period, they are all radioactive, they are breaking down of their own excessive weight, and we cannot deal with them here in terms of pattern.

The over-all pattern, however, is clear: it is a pattern of electronic structure.

The periodic table shows the configurations of 2, 10, 18, 36, 54, and 86 electrons to be remarkably stable. The nuclei of atoms having such configurations cling tenaciously to the electrons they possess but have no need or desire for more. They are, so to speak, perfectly satisfied with themselves as physicochemical entities, and in the characteristic manner of the self-satisfied in all realms, they are disinclined toward energetic activity. They refuse all offers to compete or to co-operate with atoms having electronic structures different from theirs. Content with isolation, they lie inert in a perfect peace. And though this peace seems akin to death, it has a strong appeal, in the physical as in the human world, for those who suffer the vital pangs of imbalance and incompletion. Men strive to complete themselves by satisfying their wants, or to relieve internal tensions by reducing their wants. Atoms—the atoms of the active elements—strive to complete themselves by acquiring electrons, or to balance themselves by relinquishing them, aiming always toward the stability of an inert gas. These enterprises require them to enter into co-operative arrangements with other atoms. Such arrangements are molecules.

Now, that part of quantum theory known as the Pauli Exclusion Principle explains (or describes) all this by saying that electrons are not free to arrange themselves haphazardly around the nucleus. They must instead distribute themselves in certain rigidly prescribed ways. There are only so many possible shells (which, remember, are zones where the probabilities of finding the electron are high), and each of these can contain only specific numbers of electrons. If an atom has more electrons than can fit into its innermost shells, these electrons must go into a new, incomplete shell farther out from the nucleus. If, on the other hand, an atom has precisely enough electrons to fill completely one or more shells, with no electrons left over, it has achieved a perfect balance. It then has one of the stable configurations of 2, 10, 18, etc. It is, in other words, an atom of inert gas.

Thus the first period of the periodic table contains only two elements, hydrogen and helium, because two electrons complete what has come to be known as the K shell—the shell nearest the nucleus. When an electron is added to the helium structure to make lithium, it is not permitted to join the two vibrating in the K shell but is instead forced to operate alone in a shell farther out, the so-called L shell, whose electron capacity is eight. This last accounts for the fact that the second period on the chart contains eight elements, one for each new electron added to the L shell, and ends with neon, whose ten electrons completely fill both the K shell and the L shell. The next, or third, period coincides with the initiation and completion of the M shell, also filled by eight electrons; thus argon, completing this period, has eighteen electrons distributed two, eight, eight, respectively, among its three filled shells.

But there is no need for further verbal description on this point. The following table shows at a glance the electronic structure of the inert gases—the structures which other elements strive to achieve and which, therefore, impose periodicity on chemical behavior.

	ATOMIC NO.	ELECTRON SHELLS					
		K	L	M	N	O	P
Helium (He)	2	2					
Neon (Ne)	10	2	8				
Argon (A)	18	2	8	8			
Krypton (Kr)	36	2	8	18	8		
Xenon (Xe)	54	2	8	18	18	8	
Radon (Rn)	86	2	8	18	32	18	8

To sum up, then:

Chemically active elements, striving to achieve one of these configurations, use their outer electrons—those in the incomplete and hence unstable shell—for trading purposes. Thus the hydrogen atom, with its single electron, is eager to obtain another one, thereby achieving the stable helium structure; this eagerness is what determines its chemical behavior—for instance, the fact that hydrogen atoms normally travel in linked twosomes wherein two nuclei share an electron pair, or the fact that hydrogen is highly inflammable. In combustion, hydrogen's anxiety to achieve an approximation of the helium structure is matched by oxygen's anxiety to approximate the structure of neon.

Water and the Hydrogen Bond

Now there are several ways in which outer electrons may be used to effect chemical combinations. One way is a manifestation of what is called *ionic valence* ("valence" meaning combining power) because it depends upon the ability of some kinds of atoms to give up electrons, becoming positive ions, and of other kinds of atoms to acquire electrons, becoming negative ions. (Positive ions, incidentally, are called *cations* because they are drawn to the cathode, or negative pole, of a battery; negative ions are called *anions* because they are drawn to the anode, or positive pole.) By electrostatic force (the Coulomb attraction) the ions of opposite charge are drawn to one another, and this force, which then holds the two kinds of atoms together, is called an *ionic bond*. This is the principal bond holding sodium and chlorine atoms together in crystals of sodium chloride (NaCl), or common table salt. Sodium (11), with a single electron in its outer, or M, shell, gives it up readily in order to achieve the electronic stability of neon (10), thus becoming a sodium cation (Na^+). Chlorine (17), having a single electron less than argon (18), readily attaches another electron to its outer, or M, shell in order to achieve argon's stable electronic structure. It thereby becomes a chloride anion (Cl^-). Since they have equal but opposite charges, Na^+ and Cl^- join forces (so to speak) whenever they encounter one another in favorable circumstances.

Another type of bonding arrangement, much stronger and more widespread than the ionic bond, is the so-called *covalent bond*. This is made up of a shared electron pair and is so nearly universal among chemical substances that it is sometimes referred to as *the* chemical bond. Each of the elements combining to form water exists independently in molecules containing two atoms (H_2, O_2) held together by covalent bonds. (The complexities and overlappings of bonding arrangements are such, however, as to make it possible to speak of four-atomed molecules of oxygen [O_4]: when two O_2 molecules come very close together, the attraction between them, if very weak compared to that binding two oxygen atoms into O_2, is sufficiently strong to be deemed [in this instance] a chemical bond.) It is the covalent bond that also holds together the molecules of water (H_2O).

We have indicated that each molecule of H_2 consists of two nuclei held firmly together by two electrons in an approximation, for each nucleus, of the helium structure. The motion of these two electrons, though encompassing both nuclei, is largely concentrated between them, so that the electronic structure for the molecule is commonly written H:H, with the letters indicating the nuclei and the two dots the electrons. The latter constitute the valence bond shown when we write (as chemists often do write) H–H. "We might draw an analogy with two steel balls (the nuclei) vulcanized into a tough piece of rubber (the electrons) which surrounds them and bonds them together," writes Linus Pauling, who also illustrates the arrangement as follows:

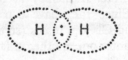

As for oxygen, you might expect its diatomic (or double-atomed) molecules to be held together by double shared-electron-pairs or covalent bonds. Each oxygen atom has six electrons in its outer, or L, shell, as symbolized by $:\ddot{O}:$.[6] If double bonds were formed, the outer shell for each nucleus would be completed with eight electrons (as in neon), thus:

[6] It is usual, in such symbolic representations, to indicate *only* the outer, or valence, electrons, ignoring the inner electrons.

$$:\ddot{O}::\ddot{O}: \quad or \quad :\ddot{O}=\ddot{O}:$$

Instead, the oxygen molecule, like the hydrogen, is held together by a *single* covalent bond:

$$:\dot{O}:\ddot{O}: \quad or \quad :\dot{O}-\ddot{O}:$$

Each molecule, therefore, has two electrons which are unpaired, and these account for the fact that O_2, whether in its liquid or solid or gaseous state, has the property of being attracted by a magnet—a property which is very rare except among metals and metallic salts.

Now the distribution of the electrons in H_2 and O_2 determines an unevenness in the distribution of the positive and negative charges within each molecule. This in turn determines a certain kind of shape of combination when hydrogen and oxygen come together to form water. The resultant molecule of H_2O* is what is called a *polar molecule* because its positive and negative charges are not spread evenly around a center but are instead distributed asymmetrically to form positive and negative poles. Figure 13 shows in a vastly oversimplified form the manner in which two hydrogen atoms are attached to an oxygen atom to make a water molecule; it may be taken, in other words, as a schematic representation of the reaction which chemists write as: $H_2 + O \rightarrow H_2O$. The equilibrium position taken by the two hydrogen atoms places them 0.95 Å from the oxygen nucleus and separates them from one another by 105 degrees

* Actually the initial formula may be assumed to be H_4O_2, since two H_2 molecules and one O_2 molecule are involved in the reaction, but we may also assume for simplicity's sake that each molecule of H_4O_2 then breaks apart immediately to produce two molecules of H_2O.

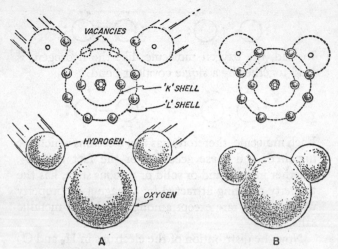

FIG. 13. *The water molecule forms in the inter-*
action of two hydrogen atoms and one oxygen atom
in the manner suggested in this simplified diagram.
It is a polar molecule because its positive and nega-
tive charges are not evenly distributed but form
positive and negative poles. The figure at B, again in
simplified terms, represents the equilibrium position
of the hydrogen and oxygen atoms, or of the positive
and negative charges, of the molecule.

of the circle (360 degrees) which we assume as the
circumference of the oxygen atom, as shown in Fig.
14. Another way of representing this is to indicate the
covalent bonds between the oxygen atom and two
hydrogen atoms as

keeping in mind that the angle H–O–H is actually 105 degrees instead of the 90 degrees here shown and that the distance separating each H from the O is 0.95 Å.

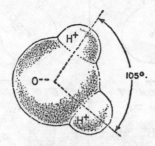

FIG. 14. *The angle of separation of the two positive charges of the water molecule is represented here.*

Water molecules may be said to have a great deal of integrity in that they maintain their identity in circumstances which cause other kinds of molecules to split into ions. Careful determinations have shown that a ton of pure water contains only about 0.1 milligrams of H^+ ions and 1.7 milligrams of OH^- ions. This means that pure water is a very poor conductor of electricity, since it provides very few charged particles to constitute a current between two electrodes. But though it resists dissociation into ions, the water molecule possesses in and by itself a good deal of ionic character, as the above figures indicate: the molecule has been described[7] as, in effect, an oxygen ion (O^-) having two hydrogen ions attached to it. This arrangement gives it a strong tendency to orient itself (or to be oriented) in an electrical field with its positive end toward the negative plate and its negative end toward the positive plate. You can readily see how this would be. Obviously (for the principle

[7] Linus Pauling (*op. cit.*, page 129).

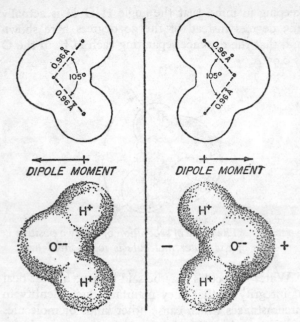

FIG. 15. *The dipole moment is a measure of the water molecule's tendency to orient itself in an electric field with its positive end toward the negative plate and negative end toward the positive plate.*

is the same as that of a lever) the strength of this tendency, which is called "dipole moment," depends upon the magnitude of the charge separation within the molecule, and in a water molecule this separation is great. Water is therefore said to have an *unusually large dipole moment* whose operations in an electric field may be illustrated as in Fig. 15.

$$H^+ + OH^- \rightleftharpoons H_2O$$

By orienting themselves in this way, water molecules tend to neutralize an electrical field—a fact expressed in technical language by saying that water's unusually large dipole moment gives it an abnormally large *dielectric constant*. If we assume the dielectric constant of a vacuum to be 1, then the dielectric constant of water is 80, which is to say that two electrical charges will attract or repel one another with only $\frac{1}{80}$ as much strength in water as they would in a vacuum.

This accounts in part for water's remarkable ability to dissolve substances, and particularly substances whose molecules are held together solely or mainly by ionic bonding. Such bonds, you'll remember, consist of the Coulomb attraction, as when Na^+ and Cl^- ions are attracted to one another to form molecules of NaCl (table salt). They are relatively weak bonds, and if they are broken at the surface of a salt crystal submerged in water, they are not likely to be re-established, since the attraction between the dissociated, oppositely charged ions is reduced by water's high dielectric constant to a fraction of what it would be in air, or to just $\frac{1}{80}$ of its strength in a vacuum. So slight an attraction can be completely frustrated by the mild thermal agitation of room temperature. We should add that the dissociation into ions is further encouraged, and new associations of them into salt crystals are discouraged, by the natural tendency of the positive ions to attach themselves to the negative, or oxygen, end of the H_2O molecules and of the negative ions to attach themselves to the positive, or hydrogen, end.

But the dipole moment of separate water molecules would by no means account for the whole of water's remarkable abilities as a solvent. To account for the latter we must introduce another concept, that of the *hydrogen bond*. This is a bond between molecules of water, molecules whose inward integrity is maintained by strong covalent bonds. By means of the *hydrogen bond, water molecules are joined to-*

gether in a community of rare tightness and continuity of structure.

There exists between *all* molecules, of whatever substance, a weak attraction which becomes significant only when the molecules are very close together. (We referred to this attraction when we spoke of two molecules of O_2 being brought together to form, in effect, a molecule of O_4.) This intermolecular force, known as the electronic *van der Waals attraction*, arises from the fact that the mutual attraction between one molecule's nucleus and another's electrons is slightly greater than the mutual repulsion of its electrons from the other's electrons and its nucleus from the other's nucleus. As a general rule, heavy molecules attract one another more strongly than light ones, which means that in general the boiling points of substances increase (are higher on the temperature scale) with their molecular weights: since it is the van der Waals attraction which must be overcome by thermal agitation before the liquid can evaporate, the amount of agitation necessary must vary directly with the strength of the attraction. You may recall that we indicated this general rule in our Chapter 1 (pages 23 and 25) without going into the reasons for it. We also indicated there that this rule, if it applied to H_2O, would fix water's freezing point at about $-100°$ C. and its boiling point at about $-80°$ C. The fact that the respective points are actually $0°$ C. and $100°$ C. is clear evidence that some force other and much stronger than the van der Waals attraction operates to bind H_2O molecules to one another.

This extra force is the afore-mentioned hydrogen bond. It is electrostatic in nature. Glance again at our schematic representation of the water molecule (Fig. 13) and you will see that the two hydrogen atoms sharing their electrons with the oxygen atom thereby expose their nuclei virtually naked to the world. Each of these exposed positive charges (the hydrogen nucleus is a single proton) exerts an attractive force upon any single, or unpaired, electron—and since oxygen's atom happens to have two such unpaired electrons, each water molecule is able to form four hydrogen bonds. Now two dipole molecules operating separately have much less ability to neutralize an electrical field than have those same two molecules bonded together in a complex. The dipole moment in the latter case is doubled. Hence water's ability to form hydrogen bonds accounts for its unusually large dielectric constant, which in turn accounts, in part, for its extraordinary capacities as a solvent.

Hydrogen bonding also accounts for the other unusual properties of water described in our Chapter 1. We have pointed to its effect on water's boiling and freezing points, and you can readily see how this effect is part and parcel of water's remarkable heat capacity and its abnormally high latent heats of fusion and evaporation. (It has been calculated that the total energy of the hydrogen bonds in a single mole —18 grams—of water is equivalent to 6000 calories.) Hydrogen bonds account for the unusual cohesive power manifested in water's high surface tension. They account, too, for water's remarkable ability to adhere strongly to a wide variety of substances, thereby "wetting" them. The process by which water wets glass, for instance, is one of forming hydrogen bonds between the exposed hydrogen nuclei of H_2O and the oxygen atoms which are part of the surface structure of glass, most glass being fused silica having the chemical formula of SiO_2. In the same way, water wets cellulose (cotton fibers, for example), clay (with most of the soil's constituents), and other substances of which oxygen atoms are an important constituent.

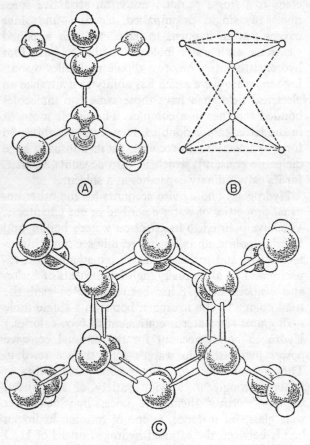

FIG. 16.   *The ice crystal is a tetrahedral structure of this general form. The large shaded spheres represent oxygen, the small white ones hydrogen.*

Further, hydrogen bonding accounts for the fact that ice floats. The peculiar arrangement of the water molecule's shared and unshared electron pairs results in its extension of bonds in four directions, and these directions are set with respect to each other at an angle equivalent to the separation of the two positive charges in the water molecule—an angle, in other words, of 105 degrees. Figure 16 shows how this dictates the geometrical form known as a tetrahedron, which is a four-sided polygon, each of whose faces is an equilateral triangle. This is the characteristic crystalline structure of ice. What happens is that water's density increases as its temperature goes down, until a point is reached (4° C.) at which the influence exerted by hydrogen bonding is stronger than the tendency to contract or shrink because of the reduced motion of the water molecules.[8] At that point, the molecules begin to arrange themselves along the directional lines of the hydrogen bonds, leaving gaps or openings between these lines. Thus the water expands (or decreases in density) until, at 0° C., it solidifies in a structure which is a very open one. The same general pattern of behavior is evidently followed in the formation of snowflakes, which are branching ice crystals grown out of moist air. Snowflakes (see Plate II) have a hexagonal, or six-sided, structure, the outline which is formed by the bases of six tetrahedrons.[9]

[8] Temperature, you'll recall from Chapter 1, is a measure of the vigor of atomic and molecular movements in a system. A reduction in temperature means a reduction in the amount of molecular movement.

[9] No one knows precisely, however, the manner in which a snowflake grows. No one can explain the amazing symmetry of its growth. This whole subject of crystals and their formation is a fascinating one, and readers who would like a pleasant introduction to it are referred to *Crystals and Crystal Growing*, by Alan Holden and Phylis Singer (Science Study Series, Doubleday, 1960).

Thus we see why—in the scientific meaning of "why"—ice floats and water wets, why water is so unusual in its heat relations and its solvent capacities. Since all these properties of water are of literally vital importance to plants and animals, and since they all depend upon hydrogen bonding, the latter might almost be deemed *the* vital bond in the same sense as covalence is often deemed *the* chemical bond. Without it, certainly, life as now lived on earth would be impossible.

CHAPTER 4

In Which We Qualify Some of the Things We've Said

Ordinary Water Is NOT Pure and Simple H_2O

Having gone this far in our explanation of the *why* of water's properties—a why which (as we pointed out on pages 64–66) is but an extended description of what water is and how it behaves—we must now qualify some of our general statements. Heretofore we have avoided qualification for fear of confusing our exposition, a danger that by now should be reduced.

First, we must qualify our statement of water's chemical composition.

We have been talking about this substance as though it were a single, simple, invariable compound whose formula is H_2O and whose molecular weight is 18.016. This, indeed, was the prevailing scientific view of it only a little over a quarter century ago. But in 1934, Harold Urey, the American physicist, discovered that the purest water obtainable contained minute portions of a substance he dubbed "heavy water" because, though having apparently the same chemical formula as ordinary water, it had a molecular weight of 20. The extra weight was due to the fact that the strange new water molecules were made of atoms of hydrogen having *twice* the atomic weight of

ordinary hydrogen, each of their nuclei containing a
neutron in addition to the single proton which is the
nucleus of ordinary hydrogen. Its properties were
found to be sufficiently different from those of ordinary hydrogen to justify a name of its own, and it is
now called *deuterium*. Its oxide, "heavy water," has
the formula D_2O. The boiling point of D_2O is a little higher than that of H_2O (it boils at 101.4° C.),
its freezing point is considerably higher than H_2O's
(it freezes at 3.8° C.), and, far from being the vital
substance that H_2O is, D_2O is physiologically inert.
Seeds watered with D_2O alone will never sprout; animals with only D_2O to drink will die of thirst.

Nor is D_2O the only substance complicating what
we formerly regarded as a single simple compound. A
third isotope of hydrogen, called *tritium*, has been
discovered. So have three isotopes of oxygen, having
atomic weights of 16 (ordinary oxygen), 17, and 18.
Of course, all the recently discovered isotopes put together make up but a tiny fraction of water. Only
minute traces of tritium are found, and the same is
true of oxygen 17, whereas deuterium is present to
the extent of only about 200 parts per million and
oxygen 18 to the extent of about 1000 parts per million. In other words, nearly all of what we call H_2O
actually is what we long believed it to be, a compound of the commonest isotopes of the two elements, with the molecular weight and chemical properties we have described. Nevertheless, since each of
the three hydrogen isotopes combines with each of
the three oxygen isotopes in the ratio of two to one,
and since each isotope ionizes in the same way as the
others, any sample of pure water must be said, for
strict accuracy, to be a mixture of no less than eighteen different molecular compounds plus fifteen different kinds of ions—thirty-three different substances
in all! (See Fig. 17.)

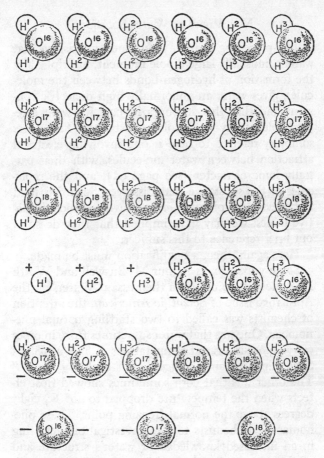

FIG. 17. *Pure water, on analysis, becomes a complicated compound indeed. It is a mixture of isotopes and ions that could be tallied as thirty-three different substances. The eighteen isotopes are represented in the top three rows of the diagram, the fifteen kinds of ions in the lower three rows.*

New Views of Water Solutions

The preceding chapter mentioned in passing that water's unusually large dipole moment, multiplied by the formation of hydrogen bonds between the molecules, gives water an abnormally high dielectric constant and that this accounts in part for water's remarkable ability to dissolve substances. The water solubility referred to here is one involving electrical attraction between water molecules, with their partially ionic character (see page 93), and the molecules of the substance that dissolves. Scientists used to believe that solubility *always* involved such attractive forces; we may have implied that they do so in our brief reference to this subject.

Here again, then, a qualification must be made.

Some years ago, as Arthur M. Buswell and Worth H. Rodebush point out in their essay "Water," in the April 1956 issue of *Scientific American,* the attention of chemists was called to two startling natural phenomena. One was that water sometimes froze in pipes carrying natural gas at temperatures as high as 68° F. Such pipes became clogged with a slushy "snow." The other was that corn sometimes showed frost effects when the temperature dropped to 40° F., eight degrees above the normal freezing point. These phenomena led chemists toward investigations resulting in an increased knowledge of water's structure and of the manner in which this structure may be distorted by the presence of substances which refuse to form ions in water or to accept water's hydrogen bonds. Nonelectrolytes, these are called—and insofar as they dissolve in water (they are very slightly soluble) the process appears to be due "not to an attraction between the substance and water but to a lack of attraction," to quote Buswell and Rodebush.

Take methane gas (CH_4), for example.

There is very little attraction between methane molecules and water molecules, yet methane is slightly soluble in water. When its dissolution was closely studied, the reaction was found to have a characteristic initially astonishing to scientific eyes. Too much heat was released. Far too much! The normal expectation is that the heat released in a reaction between solute and solvent will increase with the ease of solution. Thus the expectation was that the dissolution of methane in, say, hexane (a substance in which methane is readily soluble) would release many times as much heat as the dissolution of methane in water. Precisely the opposite was found to be true. The dissolution of methane in water releases ten times as much heat as that of methane in hexane.

Where could this heat come from? The attractive energy between the methane and water molecules was too small to account for more than a tiny fraction of it. The conclusion scientists have reached, after careful study, is that the heat is withdrawn from the water molecules which collect around the methane molecule, forming a "cage" for the latter.

The methane molecule has well over twice the volume of a water molecule. To the extent that methane dissolves in water, therefore, each of its molecules must shove aside a good many water molecules, breaking the hydrogen bonds and weakening the other attractive forces between the latter. This reduces water's normally strong inward pressures to such an extent that it may actually freeze—that is, assume a crystalline structure—at the interfaces between the water and the methane. The release of pressure, you see, amounts to a loss of heat or (the same thing) a reduction in the speed with which the water's atoms move. You observe the same phenomenon in reverse whenever you apply pressure to ice—under the runner of a skate, for instance—and cause it to melt at temperatures well below the normal melting point. A release of pressure has the opposite effect: water freezes at a higher temperature. Having crystallized, then, to form frozen hydrates, the combined methane-and-water may precipitate out of solutions.

Hence the clogging of gas pipelines with "snow" in a summer temperature.

The same sort of thing may happen at the interfaces between protein molecules and water. Any protein molecule is many, many times as large as a water molecule, and it contains large groups of atoms which, like the methane molecule, are non-polar, or non-ionic. Water has, in consequence, a strong tendency to crystallize along the surfaces of protein molecules. If this tendency is realized, as it may be in special circumstances, the abrupt expansion of the water as it becomes ice may seriously damage living tissues.

Hence the "frost damage" to corn at a temperature of 40° F.

Concerning Heavy Water and the Atomic Age

For a brief time after Urey's discovery of it, heavy water was popularly regarded as a chemical curiosity only; it had no apparent practical value. But it is illustrative of the interconnectedness of science that at the very moment Urey was making his discovery, the great Italian physicist Enrico Fermi was conducting epoch-making nuclear experiments whose results were to give to D_2O a very considerable military and economic importance.

Fermi and his collaborators in 1934 were bombarding various elements with neutrons, most of which were of high energy (speed), and the experiments were producing a whole series of artificially radioactive atoms, or *radioisotopes*, as they came to be called. (See page 82.) Fermi found that almost every normally non-radioactive element can be made radioactive—that is, transformed into a radioisotope—by neutron bombardment. He also found that the general effectiveness of neutrons in inducing radioactivity was greatly increased if the speed of the bombarding neutrons was reduced.

Like the electron and the photon of light, the neutron exhibits particle-like behavior, but its movements also show wave characteristics and quantities. It has a wavelength, which in effect is its "size," and this wavelength varies inversely with its frequency. The lower the frequency, which is the measure of neutron energy, the longer the wavelength.

There are several types of apparatus with which we can select neutrons having almost any energy we want. A low-energy neutron—one with an energy of 0.1 electron volt, say—will have a wavelength or "size" well over ten thousand times the diameter of an atomic nucleus. Obviously, a slow neutron traveling through a collection of atoms is much more likely to strike a nucleus than is a fast one. It also is more likely to be "captured" or absorbed into the nucleus it strikes.

How can the nucleus absorb something ten thousand times larger than itself? Again we must remember that we are dealing here with the neutron's wave characteristics. Inside the nucleus, the neutron acquires an energy of some fifty million volts with a consequent enormous increase in its frequency, which is inversely proportional to wavelength. As the frequency increases, the wavelength diminishes.

A neutron thus absorbed in a nucleus generally causes a nuclear imbalance with a resulting emission of rays. In other words, a radioisotope is produced. For example, ordinary aluminum is a stable element with an atomic number (or nuclear charge) of 14 and an atomic weight of 27, but when its nucleus absorbs a neutron it becomes aluminum 28, a radioisotope having the same nuclear charge but a unit more of atomic weight. Upon emission of a β-particle, or electron, and the consequent gain of a unit of positive charge on its nucleus, aluminum 27 is transformed into stable silicon 28, with atomic number 13.

Not long after Fermi and his associates made their discovery, two German scientists, Otto Hahn and F. Strassmann, found that the absorption of neutrons by the nuclei of uranium atoms resulted in the actual splitting, or fission, of these nuclei. The two fragments together had less mass than the single original nucleus—and since this difference in mass was converted into kinetic energy in the quantity predicted by Einstein's mass-energy equation,[1] the two fragments flew apart at an enormous speed. As they did they emitted, or had "boiled off" them, two or three neutrons, of which the super-heavy uranium atom has very many. Each emitted neutron might, theoretically, fission whatever fissionable nucleus it happened to strike, with the consequent release of two or three more neutrons. In other words, the fission process might become self-propagating and self-multiplying: what was called a "chain reaction" might be initiated. The potential energy releases from such a reaction could be described only as awesome.

Further experiments quickly determined that of uranium's three isotopes it was almost exclusively U^{235} (normally constituting only 0.7 per cent of the uranium) whose nuclei were split, and that U^{235} was most effectively split by slow neutrons, as Fermi's investigations indicated. Indeed, it was found that to induce a chain reaction in ordinary uranium one must

[1] $E = mc^2$, where E is energy, m mass, and c the speed of light, roughly 186,000 miles a second.

have an abundant supply of very slow neutrons. Fast neutrons—those with energies of millions of electron volts—occasionally split uranium atoms but not frequently enough to sustain a chain reaction. Neutrons of moderate energy (several electron volts) are effective splitters of U^{235}, but they are also liable to capture by nuclei of U^{238}, the isotope making up over 99 per cent of ordinary uranium. Capture by U^{238} withdraws them from circulation, so to speak, since the U^{238} does not fission but, instead, strives to stabilize itself by shooting out a single electron. (This, of course, increases the nuclear charge by one, transforming the element from uranium [atomic number 93] to plutonium [atomic number 94].) What are needed are "thermal" neutrons, so-called because their energy of about 0.02 electron volts is no greater than that of the normal thermal movement of the atoms among which they travel. Thermal neutrons are not only effective in splitting U^{235} but are also immune to capture by U^{238}, which is wholly unaffected by them. They also have a long range; their chances of knocking around among a collection of U^{238} atoms until they strike easily fissioned U^{235} are good.

All this makes it possible to produce a self-sustaining chain reaction in a mass of ordinary uranium, despite the fact that only 0.07 of it is U^{235}, provided some way can be found to slow down, or "thermalize," the fast neutrons emitted by the fission of U^{235}. A so-called "moderator" is needed, some substance which will absorb the excess energy of the neutrons without capturing the neutrons themselves.

It is here that heavy water enters the picture.

Obviously, a neutron will be abruptly slowed down if it strikes a nucleus not much heavier than itself; when it does so, it imparts some of its energy to the struck particle in the same way a billiard ball does when it strikes another. This suggests the use of hydrogen compounds as moderators, water especially; since the ordinary hydrogen nucleus (a single proton) has the same mass as a neutron, it should absorb a large part of the latter's energy in a collision. Alas for its usefulness here; the ordinary hydrogen nucleus does more than this. It often absorbs the neutron itself, becoming thereby the nucleus of a heavy hydrogen atom. Ordinary H_2O is therefore relatively ineffective as a moderator. But by the same token, the opposite is true of heavy water. Nuclei of heavy hydrogen, each consisting of a neutron and a proton, are poor neutron absorbers, but light enough to absorb large portions of the neutron's energy upon impact. D_2O, in consequence, is a highly effective moderator, as effective as any substance we know of.

Incidentally, in 1942 the British Commandos raided a certain manufacturing plant in Nazi-occupied Norway in a mysterious operation that long remained an official secret. Heavy water can be obtained in a prolonged electrolytic process involving prodigious amounts of electricity, and since hydroelectric power is abundant in Norway, it was there that the first considerable quantity of heavy water was produced. About one hundred gallons of it had been made by the winter of 1942. To prevent its falling into the hands of German scientists, who might use it as a moderator, was the purpose of the raids. Allied commanders of the secret scientific war being waged in those days were acutely aware of the danger. They knew that Fermi and his associates, at the University of Chicago, were initiating the first nuclear chain reaction in history, thus proving the feasibility of developing an atomic bomb. The nuclear fuel in this first pile was provided by the U^{235} in ordinary uranium. The moderator used was carbon in the form of very pure graphite.

Since then progress in the development of nuclear energy has increased the practical importance of heavy water. For instance, the great nuclear reactor at the U. S. Atomic Energy Commission's Argonne National Laboratory, near Chicago, uses heavy water both as moderator and as cooling agent. So does the United Kingdom Atomic Energy Authority's great reactor at Harwell, England. And the actual military as well as potential economic value of heavy water was vastly increased with the development in the early 1950s of a hydrogen bomb.

In our next chapter we are to tell a little of the present theory of the manner in which the sun converts hydrogen into radiant energy. Suffice it here to say that at very high temperatures the precise opposite of nuclear fission my occur. Heat, we repeat, is energy of motion, and as it increases beyond a certain point the nuclear energy becomes great enough to overcome the electrostatic forces which at lower temperatures cause two positive charges to repel one another. Two light nuclei—two hydrogens, say, or a hydrogen and a lithium—may thus be driven so violently into each other that the nuclear forces we spoke of in our last chapter begin to operate. A new nucleus is formed by a *fusion* of the two nuclei in what is called a thermonuclear reaction. Once initiated in a collection of light atoms, the process is chain-reacting: the nucleus formed by the fusion has slightly less mass than the two original nuclei, the difference is converted into energy in accordance with the Einstein equation, and a part of this energy is imparted to other nuclei, causing them to fuse.

But how is the initial heat to be supplied? It is a heat measured in millions of degrees of temperature, and until now we on earth have been able to produce it only for a flashing instant, through the explosion of a U^{235} or of a plutonium bomb. Every hydrogen bomb thus far exploded by the United States or Soviet Russia has been "triggered" by a fission-type bomb. But if ways can be found to generate the necessary heat economically, and with adequate controls and safeguards, nuclear fusion could some day prove superior to nuclear fission as a source of industrial power. One of its great advantages over fission is that a controlled fusion would not yield dangerous radioactive wastes. Another is that the fuel for fusion, unlike that for fission, is present in vast quantities on earth.

Nuclear theory indicated that the heavy isotopes of hydrogen are particularly "fusible"—and, indeed, the hydrogen bomb exploded in Eniwetok in 1952 is said to have consisted of a mixture of liquid deuterium and tritium, with a U^{235} bomb to trigger the thermonuclear reaction. Hence the increased importance of deuterium as the time draws near when supplies of conventional fossil fuels will be exhausted. Some experts have estimated, on the basis of known and probable reserves, that by 2000 A.D. less than one hundred years' supply of coal and oil will remain. This is on the assumption that present projections of population growth and of the increase in a per capita consumption of energy are accurate. The year 2000 is only thirty-nine years away as this is published. But there is no practical limit to the amount of fusion fuel present in the oceans of the world. The deuterium in a single gallon of sea water has an energy content equivalent to that of 350 gallons of gasoline, and there are countless thousands of millions of gallons of sea water—enough, theoretically, to supply all the energy needs of mankind for billions of years.

CHAPTER 5

Of Sun, Earth, and Water

In the beginning, the Earth was without form, and void; and darkness was upon the face of the deep; and the Spirit of God moved upon the face of the waters, commanding, "Let there be light." Then the light was divided from the dark to make the first day of creation. On the second day, God decreed the firmament amidst the waters and, using it to divide the waters that were below from the waters above, called the firmament Heaven. On the third day, all the waters were gathered into one place and dry land was caused to appear, the waters becoming the Seas and the dry land Earth, and God commanded the Earth to bring forth grass, and fruit-yielding trees, and herbs yielding seed after their own kind. This third day was peculiarly satisfying to God. When it was done and He gazed upon what He had made, He for the first time "saw that it was good."

Thus the story of the earth's creation as told in Genesis, an event occurring at nine o'clock in the morning of October 26, 4004 B.C., according to Archbishop Ussher's *Annales Veteris Testimenti*, published in 1650. The story as told by modern science lacks the archbishop's precision and differs from

Genesis in both kind and degree. Nevertheless, there are some points of similarity, as we shall see.

According to science, the "beginning" of our portion of the universe (meaning the Milky Way galaxy, of which the sun and its orbiting planets are an almost infinitesimal part) occurred between 6.5 and 7 billion years ago. Many streams of evidence, widely divergent at their first appearance, have been found to flow together to suggest this approximate date.

One such stream arises in geology, where the determination of the age of rocks has been greatly facilitated by the presence of radioactive substances. As we indicated in the preceding chapter, radioactive elements disintegrate into what are called decay, or daughter, products which are non-radioactive. Thus U^{238} (the uranium isotope whose nuclear mass is 238) breaks down ultimately into Pb^{206} (the lead isotope whose mass is 206), U^{235} breaks down into Pb^{207}, Th^{232} (thorium) breaks down into Pb^{208}, and so on. Moreover, these disintegrations occur at statistically predictable rates which are unaffected by temperature extremes, or chemical changes, or pressure variations. The measurements are taken in terms of "half lives," the length of time required for 50 per cent of the atoms of a given sample of a radioactive substance to decay into atoms of another kind. It follows that, wherever the radioactive isotope and its identifiable decay product are found together, the age of the rock since its last melting[1] can be determined by measuring the ratio of the amount of the former substance to the amount of the latter. The oldest rocks thus far found by this method (they have been found in Africa, North America, and Australia) are

[1] The qualification, "since the last melting," is important because the remelting of rocks in the earth's crust, forming what are called metamorphic rocks, is very common, and whenever it occurs the radioactive substance and its decay product are separated from one another.

2.7 billion years old; they provide us with an absolute minimum age for the earth.

But those rocks also indicate that the earth is almost certainly far older than they are, for they happen to be what geologists call "pegmatites," meaning that they occur in veins thrust into sedimentary and volcanic rocks. Since sedimentary rocks are formed by deposits of igneous rock materials previously held in suspension or solution, the presence of pegmatites indicates that erosion was already occurring more than 2.7 billion years ago. And since igneous rocks are formed by the solidification of molten magma, whereas erosion is an action of liquid water, obviously a long cooling-off period had been completed well before these dated pegmatites were formed. Join these facts to the fact that the life (that is, half life) of U^{238} is 4.5 billion years, and the latter period is strongly suggested as the approximate age of the earth's solid crust.

The same suggestion comes from a study of the lead isotopes contained in the meteorites which more or less continuously pelt the earth and whose age we assume on very good evidence to be almost the same as the earth's. These meteorites are fragments of asteroids, tiny planets that orbit between Mars and Jupiter in a belt so crowded that collisions are rather common, and the structure and composition of the fragments show beyond doubt that the asteroids from which they shattered were originally molten bodies whose interiors cooled very slowly. Some of these very solid messengers from outer space are iron meteorites, others are stony, and while the former contain practically no uranium or thorium, the latter contain definitely measurable quantities of these radioactive elements. Iron meteorites do, however, contain Pb^{206} and Pb^{207}, the lead isotopes into which U^{238} and U^{235} (respectively) break down, as well as Pb^{208}, the lead isotope into which Th^{232} breaks down. They also contain Pb^{204}, lead that is *non-radiogenic*—not formed, in other words, through radioactivity. Hence it becomes possible to determine the ratios between radiogenic and non-radiogenic lead which must have existed at the time the parent asteroid was solidified, and these ratios may then be applied to stony meteorites, in which radioactive clocks (uranium and thorium) still tick away at their known and unalterable rates. By subtracting the amount of non-radiogenic lead from the total amount of lead present, we can determine the amount of time that has passed since the stony meteorites were solidified. It turns out to be about 4.6 billion years.

This figure is in general agreement with the amount of time which would be required to place the moon where it now is with relation to the earth if it were once very near the earth (an assumption for which there is good evidence) and if its rate of recession due to tidal friction has been approximately constant (an assumption for which the evidence is more doubtful). On these assumptions, it would have taken about 4 billion years for the moon to have shifted outward to its present orbit, and, of course, both earth and moon would have had to be in existence many millions of years before the latter's recession had opened any very wide distance between the two.

Yet another very rough approximation of the age of the earth's crust derives from measurements of the amount of salt in the seas, the assumption being that the older the sea, the greater its salinity. This assumption obviously derives from the fact that water is constantly evaporating from the surface of the sea, leaving its dissolved and suspended salts behind, and that the silt-bearing rivers which empty into the sea are continuously adding more salts. To determine sea age by this method, however, one must be able to measure accurately the rate of increase in salinity at the present time and to project this rate into the past in such a way as to make allowances for wide variations in erosion and evaporation rates. (During the ice ages, for example, the rate of increase in the salinity of the North Atlantic must have been much less than it now is.) Since this is very hard to do, the resultant calculation of sea age is far from precise; it does, however, accord well with the other estimates of age we have mentioned.

But these estimates, remember, apply only to the formation of the earth's crust. Prior to this solidification there was a long period when the earth's surface was molten (a fact for which the geologic evidence is overwhelming), and prior to this a still longer period when the earth was condensing or coalescing out of an immense gaseous cloud (a hypothesis for which the evidence is very great). The three periods add up to between 6.5 and 7 billion years. This, then, is the estimated age of the earth.

It is also the estimated age of the sun.

This last may startle you who have assumed, as scientists until quite recently assumed, that the earth and other planets were born of the sun. You may be familiar with some of the theories of how this might have happened. One theory was that the sun collided with another star in an awesome catastrophe and that the planets were originally fragments shattered from the sun in the same way meteorites are shattered from colliding asteroids. Another theory, much more acceptable to science, was the so-called "ring hypothesis" espoused by the German philosopher Kant (1724–1804) and the French mathematician Laplace (1749–1827). According to this theory, the sun was originally a rather cool gaseous cloud which contracted, grew hotter as it did so, and rotated more and more rapidly until it threw out by centrifugal force successive rings of gas, which later cohered to form the planets. Yet another theory, very persuasively developed in the present century by the English physicist and astronomer Sir James Jeans, was that the planets were formed of a long filament of gaseous matter sucked from the sun's surface by the tidal force exerted by a passing star. All these theories, when worked out in mathematical detail, encountered serious difficulties having to do with the shape and spacing of the planetary orbits, the speeds of planetary rotation, the processes of gaseous concentration into solid forms, and the statistical probability (small almost to the point of impossibility) of an encounter or near encounter between two stars. The principal argument against them, however, derives from studies of stellar structure and energy production conjoined with the studies we have mentioned of the age of the earth.

For a long time we were wholly unable to provide a universally consistent explanation of the sun's radiant energy. Where did it come from? Through what processes? The English physicist Lord Kelvin suggested that the heat and light were generated in the contraction of the sun, the squeezing in of itself under the force of its own gravitation, but this explanation foundered on the calculated fact that the energy thus produced could not maintain the sun's radiation for more than about 20 million years. Similarly with attempts to explain the energy release in terms of radioactivity in the sun—the energy which could be produced in this way was but a fraction of the amount the sun has obviously expended within quite recent geologic history.

Not until Einstein came along with his relativity theory and his mass-energy equation, $E = mc^2$, could an acceptable explanation of solar energy be formu-

PLATE III. Erosion effect of a glacier is dramatically illustrated in this aerial view of multiple medial moraines piled up by Mount McKinley's Barnard Glacier, Alaska. Moraines are deposits of debris carried by glaciers. Medial moraines are formed when two valley glaciers join in a single ice stream.

Photo by Bradford Washburn.

PLATE IV. Ideal environment for formation of glaciers is seen in this Alaskan panorama, a view of Mount Hayes from the southwest. Here lies the source of the Susitna River, the trickle visible in the central foreground. *Photo by Bradford Washburn.*

lated. The sun's energy, it was at once realized, must be atomic in origin and might be produced either by the total annihilation of matter, whereby proton–anti-proton and electron-positron pairs canceled each other out in intense flashes of energy or by the fusion of hydrogen atoms to make heavier atoms, a process in which only a fraction of the matter involved is transformed into energy. The amount of energy which would be released in matter annihilation is almost beyond belief. "From an ounce of coal we should obtain sufficient energy to run engines of a total horsepower of 100,000 for one year . . . ," writes H. Spencer Jones, the British astronomer.[2] "If annihilation of matter provided the source of the energy of the stars, they would be able to maintain their output of energy without very serious diminution for millions of millions of years." But he also points out that, theoretically, the process could occur only at temperatures of billions of degrees centigrade, whereas the highest temperatures reached in the interior of stars has been estimated at around twenty million degrees.

Scientists therefore turned to the alternative proposal, which now is generally accepted. It has been demonstrated that a particular cycle of reactions, involving nitrogen and carbon as catalysts (that is, as agents which affect reactions without being themselves affected) and occurring over and over again, would build helium out of hydrogen in the sun at the rate necessary to maintain the radiation. When the helium atom is built of four hydrogen atoms, it weighs $139/140$ as much as the hydrogen atoms weighed; it is this missing $1/140$ of mass, transformed into energy, which is the basic unit of the sun's radi-

[2] *Life on Other Worlds* (Mentor Book, New American Library, 1949, page 148).

ant energy, as it is of the destructive power of the hydrogen bomb.

But the acceptance of the hydrogen-fusion hypothesis places a severe limit on the present age of the sun—severe, that is, compared to the millions of millions of years in which this age might be computed if mass annihilation were assumed as the source of its energy. It would appear that the sun and the other stars in our system—if we may judge from their present size, brightness, motion, and relation to each other; and from their composition, as revealed by analyses of their spectra—can be little if any older than our earth and the other planets. This in turn suggests that all were formed almost simultaneously in a single gigantic creative process. Astronomers (most of them) seem more and more convinced of it as they spin their eon-capturing webs of mathematics and probe the depths of space with telescopes far more powerful than any ever made before.

So much for the age of our world. What of the creative process itself?

Four Theories

Out of the welter of theorizing and argument have emerged four general hypotheses which, though they differ greatly from one another, are alike in retaining enough points of similarity with the Biblical story to make the latter seem a poetic metaphor for what actually occurred. Three of the hypotheses agree that in the beginning, some seven billion years ago, the universe[3] was indeed without form, and void, and

[3] One of the four hypotheses has to do with the creation of the whole *universe*—that is, of all the matter there is. The others, insofar as they agree with the first hypothesis and with vague aspects of the Biblical story, are limited to the island universe, the particular galaxy, of which our solar system is a part.

darkness was upon the face of the deep. They further agree that this initial "deep" must be envisaged as an ocean, not of water, but of primordial chaos having gaseous properties, and that something "moved" upon and within it to produce light, the immense light of a heat great enough to effect, and be affected by, all manner of transmutations and combinations of the primitive material. The hypotheses disagree, however, and widely, in their description of the nature of the primordial chaos and of the manner in which order was born of it.

One of the four, associated with the name of George Gamow,[4] pictures the original "deep" as a super-hot gas having a density beyond any solid material ever directly observed by men. It may seem strange to you that such a substance could be deemed a gas, but the latter is a state defined, you will remember, in terms of its lack of rigid structure, its compressibility, and the randomness of the movements of its constituent particles; by these terms the primitive stuff, which Gamow dubbed *Ylem*, was certainly gaseous, though it also had liquid properties. Dense and hot though it initially was, it further contracted until its subatomic particles were packed into a mass more than 240,000,000,000,000 times as dense as water and having surface-tension forces 1,000,000,-000,000,000,000 times greater than those of water. It formed a sphere whose radius was equivalent to only eight sun's radii, yet contained all the stuff of all the island universes that now wheel, with their millions

[4] Gamow, now physics professor at the University of Colorado, is the author of four popular books about the physical and biological world as described by contemporary science, books in which he gives his theory of creation. All are available as paperbacks published by Mentor Books, New American Library. Their titles: *The Biography of the Earth, The Birth and Death of the Sun, One Two Three . . . Infinity*, and *The Creation of the Universe*.

of millions of stars, across billions of light-years of space.[5] A fraction of a cubic inch of it would have weighed more than a hundred million tons!

The pressures which developed within this undifferentiated "nuclear fluid" (for Gamow's picture is, in effect, of a single giant atomic nucleus) were quite incredible, and they very soon reached a point where further increase—a further compression of the fluid, in other words—was impossible. At that point the contracting forces of gravitation and surface tension were suddenly overbalanced by the intense pressures of internal radiation. There was a reaction—and what a reaction! The whole concentrated universe exploded in such a blaze of light and heat as can never again occur, reducing the density of its stuff to about a million times that of water within two seconds, and to that of water within a few hours. By this time all the elements, even the heaviest and most complex of them, would have been created. As a matter of fact, they all would have been formed within the first thirty minutes of the explosion's intense heat. By this time, too, the expanding gas, being gravitationally unstable, may already have begun to thicken in certain core areas and to thin out in areas between the cores. The process thus initiated led to separation of vast areas into spheres of cooling gas and finely dispersed dust. These spheres continued to expand in their over-all dimensions while widening the space between themselves and their neighbors; at the same time they began to break down into myriads of smaller spheres.[6] The latter, as they gathered more

[5] A light-year is the distance which light travels in a year. Since its speed is 186,000 miles per second, a light-year is about 6,000,000,000,000 miles.

[6] If this abruptness of creation seems incredible in view of the immensities of time and space through which the universe has evolved, one must remember that birth and death are always sudden events, no matter how many years lie between

and more matter into themselves, increasing their densities and by that token their internal pressures, grew hotter and hotter until they were luminous globes consisting at the outset of approximately 1 per cent iron and other heavy elements; 1 per cent nitrogen, carbon, and oxygen; 5 per cent or less helium; and the rest (93 per cent or more) hydrogen. As these stars condensed, some of the material out of which they cohered remained outside of them, forming (in Gamow's words) "a giant rotating envelope" of gas within which were dust particles of "terrestrial" material. The latter, through collisions whereby smaller particles were buried in larger ones, formed growing lumps of solid matter which in our solar system became the earth and other planets. (Gamow is here accepting a theory proposed by the German physicist Weizsäcker, who calculated mathematically that the aggregation process would have been completed within approximately 100 million years.)

Thus the formation of galaxies, vast systems of stars and relatively infinitesimal star-orbiting planets having sufficient gravitational stability to maintain distinct identities as they wheel, slowly turning upon

them. Nor is the universal birth which Gamow envisages much less amazing, on the face of it, than the observed fact that stars, after billions of years of flaming life, do now and then destroy themselves within a few hours in tremendous explosions called supernovae. They then dissolve into vastly spreading clouds of luminous, slowly cooling gas. Indeed, supernovae have been explained by some scientists as resulting from a process very like that which Gamow suggests for universal creation. According to this explanation, the star abruptly collapses, shrinking its radius to as little as 1 per cent of its former value in half an earth-day and compressing its interior thus swiftly into virtually undifferentiated "nuclear fluid." At this point, the intensity of the internal radiation blows away the star's outer layers, releasing the immensely expansive energies of the fluid, which, as it increases in volume, splits into separate nuclei and electrons, forming (perhaps within minutes) atoms of all the stable chemical elements.

their axes, along stupendous corridors of space. Thus, too, an explanation of the apparent motion of these galaxies with relation to each other.

This last seems, at first glance, very strange indeed; all the galaxies seem to be rushing away from ours, and from each other, at rates of speed which increase with their distance from us and from each other. Why do we think so? One of the peculiarities of light is that its color shifts toward the violet end of the spectrum when its source is approaching the observer and toward the red end when its source is moving away, and that the amount of shift varies with the speed of the light source's approach or retreat. The *Doppler effect* this is called, and it is markedly evident in galactic spectra: the farther away a galaxy is from us, the greater the "red shift" in its spectrum, and hence, inferentially, the greater the speed of recession. Scientists have concluded from this that the universe as a whole is expanding, with the result that the galaxies move away from each other just as painted dots on a toy balloon would move apart as you blew up the balloon. And this expansion is, of course, a continuing effect of the original universal explosion, according to Gamow's hypothesis.

Less spectacular in its initial effects than the "big bang" creation, though perhaps more startling in its philosophical implications, is the process envisaged by the British astronomer-mathematician Fred Hoyle and his associates. He rejects the assumption of a First Cause or Prime Mover, which is clearly implicit in Gamow's cosmology, and prefers to believe that the universe *as a whole* is eternal: having had no beginning in time, it can have no end. It is also infinite; if we could travel to the farthest boundary we could possibly set for it, we would look out into a beyond as extensive and as full (or empty) of matter-and-energy as the space our far boundaries enclosed. The reason for this is that matter is being continuously created out of, literally, nothing. It is being created, as it has always been and always will be, at the average rate of a single atom a year in a space equivalent to that occupied by a skyscraper of average size! This is a rate far below any possibility of direct observation by men but sufficient to account for all the matter found within the observable spatial and temporal universe. Indeed, within these limits "the total rate . . . is about a hundred million, million, million, million, million tons per second," writes Hoyle, so enormous is the space involved.

Hoyle finds several reasons for preferring continuous creation to the "big bang" theory. For one thing, the latter is inexpressible in mathematical language, whereas the former can be presented in precise equations whose consequences may be worked out and checked against experimental observations. For another, continuous creation is really much less incredible than the sudden-explosion idea, since it avoids questions as to what went on before the beginning, what will go on after the end, and what lies beyond outermost space—questions which the human mind, structured as it is, cannot avoid asking. Third, continuous creation provides answers to questions raised by the explosion hypothesis. For example, if the universe is expanding as a result of a single violent act of creation seven billion years ago, how and why did it happen that gaseous matter whirled in upon itself and condensed into galaxies? Hoyle finds unsatisfactory the mathematical descriptions of the alleged process by which this occurred, whereas the contradiction is removed if we assume that "the new material produces an outward pressure that leads to a steady expansion" and that irregularities are produced in this "background material" by the gravitational fields of the galaxies, causing the new matter to "give a steady supply of new galaxies."[7] Another question: If hydrogen is being continuously consumed in huge quantities within every star, as quite obviously it is, how does it happen that the universe "is nevertheless overwhelmingly composed of it"? The explosion hypothesis suggests no answer, whereas continuous creation simply assumes that the freshly made atoms are atoms of hydrogen, the simplest and lightest element out of which all others are made.

According to Hoyle, then, our particular galaxy began (in a universe which as a whole is without beginning or end) as an immense, flat rotating disk of hydrogen gas drawn together by gravitational forces which had isolated it from other disks of a precisely similar nature, disks separated more and more widely from one another as new atoms came into being between them. Our particular gaseous disk (like all the others) was much too large and diffuse to be gravitationally stable. As it turned upon its axis, concentrations were formed within it, to each of which was imparted, by the over-all rotation, an angular momentum. (Angular momentum is one of the fundamental concepts of physics. In its simplest form it is defined as the product of a body's mass, angular velocity, and distance from the axis of rotation, or mvr, where m is mass, v velocity and r radius.) These eddies of gas became separate whirling clouds which in turn broke down into smaller whirling clouds, each denser and hotter than its parent, until at last the stars were born —luminous bodies whose interior energy was great enough to resist further contraction and to balance the energy lost through surface radiation. One such star was our sun.

But (again according to Hoyle) our sun at birth was no solitary child; it had a brother, who was con-

[7] On page 126 of his *The Nature of the Universe* (Harper, 1950).

siderably larger, and much less stable. The two made up what is known to astronomy as a binary system. Such systems are very common. Nearly half of all the stars occur in pairs, though the distances between the companion stars vary enormously. Sometimes this distance is as great as a tenth of a light-year, sometimes as little as a fraction of a light-minute, and in order to account for what happened when it blew up, it has been calculated that the sun's companion must have been about one light-hour from the sun. For, according to this theory, it did blow up. It became a supernova, exploding most of its substance into interstellar space at speeds of several million miles an hour and radiating more light for a few days than all the other of our galaxy's ten billion stars put together. The fraction of the original star that remained intact recoiled from our sun, as in the initial jet propulsion of a rocket, and as it began its journey, it sent out in farewell salute to the companion of its youth a streamer of gas which was caught and held in the sun's gravitational field. This gaseous cloud, cooling and spreading into a flat disk rotating around the sun, had an atomic composition far different from the sun's, for it contained atoms of the heaviest, most complex nuclei, formed within a few minutes by nuclear fusion at a temperature some 300 times as great as that in the sun's interior. The cloud was unevenly distributed, being denser in some areas than in others. It was also very cool, having temperatures well below the freezing point of water. And within it molecular combinations of atoms were formed through chemical reactions. These molecules, as was pointed out by Sir Harold Jeffreys and A. L. Parsons, "must have collected into a swarm of solid bodies by a process similar to the formation of water drops in the clouds of our own terrestrial atmosphere."

There were, of course, frequent collisions between

these bodies at speeds causing most of them to disintegrate sooner or later into the gaseous state, but a very few managed to escape such accidents long enough to grow into solid spheres having radii of about one hundred miles. At this critical point the chief agency of growth ceased to be the slow condensation process; it became instead the gravitational field created by the solid body itself as it spun through space; and the growth of each body became thereafter much more rapid as it sucked into itself the gases and cosmic dust through which it passed. Hoyle refers to calculations that a billion years would have been required to grow a body as large as the earth, but that the increase from this size to that of the largest planet, Jupiter—which has a diameter some 11 times the earth's and a mass more than 317 times the earth's—would have taken only 100,000 years. Why, then, did the earth stop growing? Did it run out of food? No, it didn't, replies Hoyle, who goes on to explain that the earth cannot truly be said to have stopped growing, since, in actual fact, it never grew. What happened was that the "primordial condensations" did grow at a constantly accelerating rate until they had packed into themselves practically all the matter that had been in the original disk and had achieved masses considerably greater than Jupiter's, all the while continuing to cool and grow more dense. They then encountered another critical point—the size beyond which a compact body cannot maintain its integrity while rotating as rapidly as these masses were.[8] (They completed a rotation in less than seven

[8] This critical point virtually coincided with that at which the weight of a solid body's outer layers must produce internal collapse by literally smashing the atoms of the interior. An Indian astrophysicist, D. S. Kothari, has estimated in terms of current atomic theory that a weight of about 150 million pounds per square inch would crush atoms; this weight is very closely approached in the heart of Jupiter. "Thus," writes

hours, it has been estimated.) At this point they broke into what Hoyle calls "blobs" of matter, some of which became satellites of the largest planets and some of which managed to escape the parent body's gravitational field and achieve orbits around the sun exclusively their own. The earth was among the latter "blobs." Closely associated with it was the much smaller "blob" which became our moon.

Hoyle's estimate is that this culminating (for us) event of creation, the birth of the earth, occurred about 4 billion years ago.

The third theory of creation, as summarized by Gerard P. Kuiper[9] of the Yerkes Observatory, Chicago, is in several respects similar to those we have sketched. It does not presume to describe the origin of everything, nor does it assert eternalness for the universe as a whole, but it agrees that the sun was formed of a cold interstellar cloud, a *protostar*, which drew in upon itself as it wheeled through space. It continued to contract through a period of about 80 million years, shrinking at last to about one ten-millionth of its initial dimensions—and not until the last few of these millions of years, when its diameter was about that of the present orbit of Mercury, did it begin to shine feebly. By this time, a small fraction (about 6 per cent) of the total mass had somehow become separated from the rest; it formed a "solar nebula" rotating around the sun, and since the sun was still a dark star, and since the nebula steadily lost

Gamow on page 148 of his *The Birth and Death of the Sun* (Mentor Books, New American Library, 1952), "Jupiter represents geometrically the largest piece of cooled matter that can in principle exist in the universe." If the primordial body had not flown apart before it collapsed to a fraction of Jupiter's dimensions, the earth, of course, could not have been formed, by this theory.

[9] In *The Earth and Its Atmosphere* (Basic Books, 1957), an anthology edited by D. R. Bates, F.R.S., in connection with the International Geophysical Year, 1957–58.

heat by radiation into interstellar space, this nebula became a very cold gas indeed. As a matter of fact, its temperature sank to less than 50° C. above absolute zero[10] while, as a part of the same process, its density increased until it had become (relatively) a very thin flat disk which was gravitationally unstable. The disk was then broken up by gravitational forces into a number of separate gaseous clouds, or protoplanets, one of which was Protoearth.

Protoearth was a very cold, disk-shaped cloud at first, containing about 500 times as much matter as the earth now contains and having a diameter nearly 1800 times that of the earth. For the most part it was a cloud of gas. Ninety-nine per cent of its atoms were of hydrogen and helium, but neon, methane, and ammonia were also present, and there were even traces of water vapor. Most of the water in the cloud, however, was frozen into snow and made up part of the solid material which drifted through the cloud as a fine dust. This dust, its grains growing in diameter through the condensation process described by Jeffreys and Parsons, spiraled inward through millions of years toward the center of the disk, where was formed, at last, the solid earth.

Finally, a fourth promising theory, which seems to resolve some of the difficulties of the other three, has been proposed by Professor Hannes Alfvén of Stockholm's Institute of Technology. His theory derives from what is called "magneto hydrodynamics," the science of ionized gases in a magnetic field. Alfvén's initial point is that only in a relatively tiny portion of the universe, and only under very special conditions, do atoms behave according to the laws of ordinary fluids (hydrodynamics), as they do on earth. Else-

[10] Absolute zero is −273.18° C., at which temperature point all effective atomic and molecular motion ceases.

where, most matter exists in the form of ionized gases.

Now in the days of creation, according to Alfvén, when the sun formed the center of an intensely hot, ionized cosmic cloud, the sun's magnetic field warded off the portions of the electrically charged cloud which were farthest from it. As these cooled, some of their atoms acquired electrons, becoming electrically neutral. These began to fall toward the sun, accelerating to enormous speeds as they moved through millions of miles. Sooner or later they collided with atoms of the gas nearer the sun, became ionized again, and again were halted and held off by the sun's magnetic field. The process was selective. Elements most easily ionized were the ones halted farthest from the sun; those ionized with greater difficulty came nearer the sun. Thus the original cosmic cloud became separated into smaller clouds orbiting in concentric circles about the sun. The cloud farthest from the sun cooled the most rapidly; as it cooled, some of the atoms coalesced to form particles of dust, which in turn coalesced to make larger and larger solids, eventually forming Jupiter, Saturn, Uranus, and Neptune. Another cloud, nearer the sun, formed Mars and our moon. This primordial cloud initially overlapped the edge of the cloud nearest the sun, whence came Mercury, Venus, and Earth.

Water as Geologic Force

The earth was at one time, very early in its history, a molten mass radiating heat into surrounding space. The geologic evidence of it seems to most scientists overwhelming. And there is also close agreement among scientists as to how and why the earth gradually heated up as it condensed. One factor was the release of gravitational energy as a result of compac-

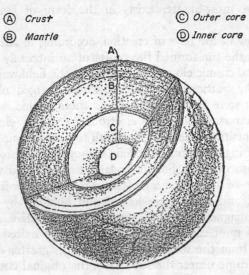

Ⓐ *Crust*　　　　Ⓒ *Outer core*
Ⓑ *Mantle*　　　　Ⓓ *Inner core*

FIG. 18.　*The earth is not a homogeneous structure but a layered one that in cross section would look something like this, according to current theory.*

tion (a subject outside the scope of this book); another was radioactivity, then some fifteen times more intense on earth than it now is. There were yet other factors, all operating to melt the frozen sphere at a time when it spun upon its axis more rapidly than it now does.[11] Centripetal and centrifugal forces, and convection currents in the viscous liquid mass, separated the planetary substance into distinct concentric zones during the melted period. In time the earth was structured (Fig. 18) into a still-molten inner core of heavy matter (mostly iron, with some nickel and perhaps some silicates) surrounded by layers of lighter

[11] Tidal friction exerted by the moon's gravitational force acts as a brake on the earth's rotation, lengthening the day at the present rate (according to one estimate) of one second every 120,000 years. The molten earth's day may have lasted only three or four hours.

material, the outermost of which was a mantle of basalt several hundred miles thick, topped by a thin crust only six to twenty-two miles thick. There are reasons for believing that the mantle began to freeze from the bottom up, thus delaying for some millions of years the formation of the solid crust. The latter event began geologic history, as we have said, some 4.5 billion years ago.

By this time, the earth had lost all but a tiny fraction of the gases which had originally enveloped it. When solidification began, the sphere must have been nearly as devoid of atmosphere as the moon now is. This was a consequence of the great melting and freezing processes, during which vast quantities of heat were released into surrounding space. As the original gaseous envelope absorbed the heat, the constituent molecules moved faster and faster until their average velocities must have approached two miles a second. This is well above the speed at which the escape of gases from the earth's gravitational field becomes rapid; it has been calculated that if the average molecular velocity in an atmosphere exceeds one fourth of the planet's escape velocity (7.1 miles per second), that atmosphere will be dissipated into outer space within a relatively short time. Gone, then, were the hydrogen and helium which had made up all but 1 per cent of the original atmosphere. Except for traces, the poisonous methane and the original atmospheric oxygen, nitrogen, and water vapor were gone, too. Of even the heaviest inert gases scarcely a trace remained.

This extreme poverty of air did not, however, last long, relatively speaking. Gases bubbled up through the molten magma, they shot up through fissures in the growing islands of solid stuff, they were lifted by evaporation from hot surfaces, and they formed a new atmosphere which the earth was soon cool enough to retain. It was an atmosphere far different from that which the earth had lost, and different, too, from that which the earth now has. There was very little free oxygen in it; there was much carbon dioxide; there were enormous quantities of water vapor.

Had we been able to look at the earth from, say, Venus in those far-off days, we would have seen it shining as one of the brightest objects in all the night sky—assuming for the moment against all evidence that the rest of the sky was then as it now is. Through the most powerful telescopes, even, the earth would have looked to us very much as Venus looks to us today, for, like Venus now, so then was the earth wrapped in an unbroken mantle of cloud whose dazzling white outer surface reflected about 60 per cent (compared to about 7 per cent for the moon) of all the sunlight falling upon it. And of the absorbed 40 per cent, no visible ray reached the earth's surface, so thick was the globe-encircling cloud, so dense its texture. Hidden from outer space for thousands upon thousands of years were the lurid scenes of earth-crust formation, such scenes of ceaseless fire and flame-shot smoke and rolling billows of steam as medieval superstition devised for hell. The energies of radio-active elements trapped beneath the solidified surface remelted the lower rocks, producing stupendous eruptions of glowing lava. Mountains were heaved up as unevennesses in the density of solidification caused the crust to buckle, and huge portions of the global surface were depressed into basins as the weight of the solid surface material caused supporting structures to collapse.

All this, from the point of view of the present book, was a gigantic setting of the stage on which water was to play a stellar role. And all the while it was going on, water hovered in the wings, or, as one had better say, on the wing, awaiting its cue to enter. It waited with a growing impatience. It had, indeed, to be continuously shoved back with angry heat as more and more of it condensed into raindrops pressing persistently downward from the thickening cool layer of the upper atmosphere, striving to enter actively into the surface scene. At long last, near the beginning of the longest and darkest night that the earth has thus far known, rain fell upon a surface sufficiently cool to permit it to run off as liquid water from higher places to lower instead of instantly vaporizing. From that moment on, through months and years and hundreds of years, the rain fell in torrents, ceaselessly, its intensity increased whenever newly exposed surfaces shot carbon dioxide and fresh water vapor and clouds of corrosive gases into the air.

Slowly, the globe-encircling mantle of cloud was thinned; slowly, the blackness of night gave way to a twilight gloom; until the mantle was torn apart here and there, and at last wholly dissipated over wide areas, to permit sunlight to fall through clear air upon the earth's damp face. Indeed, most of the light fell upon an actually liquid face, for by this time every depressed area of the surface had been filled up with water. The first seas had been formed. They were virtually fresh-water seas upon which the sun first shone: they contained only minute traces of mineral salts, but these traces were clear evidence that the rock-grinding, soil-making, landscape-molding forces of water— its power to dissolve and erode—were already under way. From then until now these forces have been at work every instant of every day, wearing down mountains, eating away whole continents, aiming always to reduce the earth's crust to a perfect smoothness. If the aim were finally achieved, the face of our planet would be an unbroken ocean some two or three miles deep—but, of course, it never is finally achieved, though it is probable that most of the earth's surface has been covered by sea most of the time since the crust solidified. The wearing down is counteracted by a building up of surfaces. After (or while) old mountains are reduced to level plains and the plains wash into the sea, subterranean forces heave new high plains above the waters, thrust new mountains up into the clouds, and water has all its work to do over again.

We now are able to see how water's peculiar properties, accounted for by hydrogen bonding, have made it by far the most important of all terrestrial agencies for the geologic modification of the earth's surface.

Consider, *first*, the important role played by water's abnormally high latent and specific heats in the cooling of the solidifying crust. The original cloud mantle soaked up heat in vast quantities and carried it to the upper atmosphere, where it was released into outer space as the water froze. The energy which held up the curtain of rain and kept it from touching the hot surface through century after century was energy drawn from that surface, which in the process cooled.

Consider, *second*, how water's abnormally high surface tension increases its erosive ability. We have said that this tension causes a falling drop of water to form an almost perfect sphere, one which resists deformation, and that the surface seems to snap around the drop as if it were an elastic membrane. The surface, in other words, is hard and rough, so that every drop of rain, especially when driven on a high wind, is a tiny but highly effective bullet, which can shatter minute fragments out of even the hardest rock. As for the water which runs off the surfaces into streams and rivers, it has an abrasive force by virtue of the solid materials it carries along. The amount of this force— the number and unit weight of the materials which the water can carry—varies with the stream's rate of flow, of course. Double the latter and you increase by sixty-four times the massiveness of the rocks a stream can transport. A mountain torrent can dislodge and tumble large boulders along its bed, using these to grind and shatter other rocks along the way.

Consider, *third*, the manner in which water's unusual capacities as a solvent and its remarkable ability to "wet" other substances (an ability which involves, you remember, the forming of hydrogen bonds between water molecules and molecules of matter with which they come in contact) join with high surface tension to increase its effectiveness as erosive agent. In the early days, after portions of the original rock crust had been pummeled and ground into dust, this erosiveness was relatively greater over the globe as a whole than it now is, for the resistance to erosion was then much lower. The primitive "soil" of those days was but a loose collection of mineral particles, lacking the cohesive effect of organic matter; it was therefore much more vulnerable to solution and suspension in water than today's soil is. But the general process of soil erosion was then the same as it now is. When a raindrop strikes naked soil, it gouges a dent as it flattens out and shatters into pieces. At the same time, surface tension makes each of the smaller drops strive at once to assume the minimum-surface-area shape, which in turn causes them to bounce like so many rubber balls into the air. As their surfaces snap like elastic membranes around them, fine particles of soil are scooped up. If the water then runs off the surface, it carries this soil with it. Moreover, the suspended fine material tends to increase the proportionate amount of runoff from a bare soil, for it tends to clog the soil pores through which, otherwise, more rain could be absorbed. "Puddling" is the technical name for the process.

Consider, *fourth*, how freezing water's remarkable behavior, with the consequent open structure of ice crystals, operates to make soil, transport rock and soil materials, and in general mold the earth's surface. You may be familiar with the fact that pioneers of New England, as they cleared land for farming, often used water to split granite boulders apart. They bored holes in the boulders, unless cracks already existed there, and they filled them with water, which, freezing and expanding into ice as winter cold came on, broke the boulders asunder. Nature makes use of the same process. It has done so ever since that night early in earth history when the temperature dropped for the first time below 0° C. atop a young mountain and froze the water trapped in some rocky depression. Nor is the effectiveness of water as rock fragmenter and soil grinder limited to its expansiveness at, and immediately above, its freezing point. After it has frozen in bulk to form glaciers, as it does on mountaintops and has in the past done over large portions of what are now temperate zones, it becomes a very potent erosive force. (Plate III.) This is because glaciers flow. They flow more ponderously than liquid water does, and in somewhat different ways, but they flow to much the same geologic effect. They grind up rock as they move; they gouge indentations in the surface over which they travel; they transport vast quantities of rock-and-soil material. The largest and fastest of them wears away an inch of solid material every two years, or four feet every century. This is a slow erosion rate compared to that produced by heavy rains upon steep slopes of loose and naked soil, but it is a very rapid process compared to geologic processes in general. It is rapid enough to reduce a high mountain to level plain within the twinkling of an eye, if that eye be one of geologic time.

And why do glaciers flow? Because of the open structure which solid water assumes in consequence of hydrogen bonding. The "bridges" whereby ice crys-

FIG. 19.   *Ice flow around a solid object makes an interesting home experiment. Loop a length of fine wire around an ice cube and suspend a weight from the wire as in the illustration. Place the apparatus in the freezing compartment of your refrigerator. In time the wire will pass through the cube, which will stay in one piece.*

tals are joined to one another to form lattice structures are weak points which collapse under high pressures. The pressure upon ice at a glacier's base is high indeed. Hence the "bridges" collapse to produce water which is liquid at temperatures considerably below 0° C., and this supercooled water lubricates the glide of solid ice pressing upon it. When the temperature is relieved, the cold liquid promptly solidifies and remains solid until pressure again breaks down the lattice structure. "Regelation," this process is called, and it not only helps a glacier to flow but also enables it to flow around solid objects, or (it amounts to the same thing) enables these solid objects to pass through the glacier without cutting it in two. You may see for yourself (Fig. 19) how this process works by setting a cube of ice on some kind of frame, looping over the cube a length of fine wire to which a weight is attached, and placing the whole apparatus in the freezing compartment of your refrigerator. You'll find that the wire will pass through the ice cube, which afterward is as solid and single as before.[12] What happens is that the weighted wire melts the ice on which it presses and then squeezes the supercooled liquid around it, whereupon the liquid promptly freezes solid again.

Closely associated with regelation in glacial flow is a process known as "translation." It, too, derives from ice's open structure, but it differs from regelation in that it does not involve a complete melting of crystals, but only a partial one; enough of the bonds in the crystalline lattice are broken to give the ice plastic qualities, enabling planes of crystals to slide in a straight line over and beneath one another. The flow to this extent is a glide lubricated not only by the compressed liquid beneath the ice but also by such clay as may lie in the glacial bed, clay rendered plastic by the thorough soaking it receives from the liquid water.

We dwell thus upon ice and glaciers as geologic forces because they have been of major importance for periods of thousands of years in the earth's recent geologic history, determining many of the most characteristic landscape features upon many thousands of square miles of land. The founders of geological science, in the eighteenth and early nineteenth centuries, were much puzzled by the occurrence over wide areas of Europe and North America of so-called "drifts" of "till." These consisted of mixtures of boulders, gravel, clay, and sand which quite obviously had

[12] Alan Holden and Phylis Singer, in their *Crystals and Crystal Growing* (Science Study Series, Doubleday, 1960, page 223), say that in one such experiment a #30 wire carrying a 1¼-pound weight traveled three fourths of an inch through ice in two hours.

been scooped up somewhere else and carried to their present locations. But what agency could have done this transporting job? It must have been huge in size and stupendous in energy, for the quantity of the deposited materials was immense. The answer was given in 1840 by Louis Agassiz, who was intimately acquainted with the Alpine glaciers of his native Switzerland and their effects upon the land they had covered and from which they had now retreated. He demonstrated conclusively that an ice sheet many thousands of feet thick, and even miles thick in places, had once covered most of northern Europe, Canada, and the northern half of the United States.

What are now lush plains and valleys, green and warm under summer suns, then presented to a continuously wintry sky the aspect which only Greenland and Antarctica, of all large land masses, wear continuously today (Fig. 20). Millions of cubic miles of water, withdrawn from the oceans, were frozen into these stupendous masses of ice, lowering sea levels all over the earth by more than three hundred feet and so weighting down parts of the earth surface that they were depressed by hundreds of yards into their plastic substructures. In the Great Lakes region, for instance, the land was depressed by more than two hundred yards. When the ice retreated northward, sea water flooded into the depressions, and when these seas in turn departed, thrust back by the spring of the earth surface after the weight of ice was removed, they left behind much marine debris, including the skeletons of whales, upon what are now dry-land elevations of several hundred feet in Michigan and northern New York. The Great Lakes themselves, and the tens of thousands of lakes in Minnesota, Wisconsin, Michigan, and New England, are mementos of the glaciation.

There seem to have been at least four, and proba-

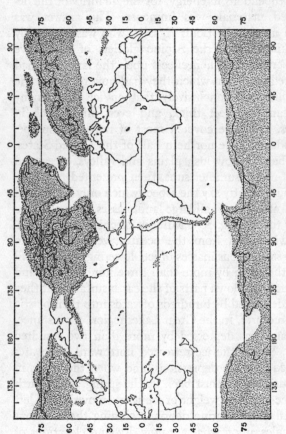

FIG. 20.   In the ice ages glaciers spread over the shaded areas shown in this map. The last major glaciation began perhaps 130,000 years ago.

bly many more, great ice ages in the last million years or so, interspersed with periods of scores of thousands of years when the world was considerably warmer than it is today. There were also fluctuations—advances and retreats of the ice pack—during each ice age. The last major glaciation has been estimated to have begun a little over 130,000 years ago and to have been divided into three distinct periods. During the first of these, which lasted some 30,000 years, ice pushed southward from Arctic regions until it covered all Canada and at least the northern tier of the United States. Then came an intermission of some 60,000 years when the climate moderated enough to force a partial retreat of the ice, but not enough to permit a lush vegetation to grow across the North Temperate Zone. Temperatures varied from cool to bitter cold; precipitation, whether as snow or rain, was severely limited; and across the bleak landscape marched stupendous clouds of dust as the winds snatched up great handfuls of naked earth and laid them down again to form deposits of what geologists now call loess, a soil type which erodes in vertical banks whereas other types erode in sloping planes. About 40,000 years ago this intermission ended. The climate grew colder; the ice again crept southward, though not as far as it had before; and this last ice epoch did not enter its final stage until about 25,000 years ago. It has not yet ended. We live today in the waning years of the most recent ice age as the glaciers of Greenland and Iceland and the highest mountains elsewhere slowly retreat. When, or if, a new ice age will come, we cannot say.

We cannot say, because we do not know what causes ice ages. Not with any certainty. We do know, from a study of deposits laid down during "recent" mountain-making revolutions (the Caledonian of some 300 million years ago; the Appalachian of 150

million years ago), that ice ages occur only after new
mountains have been thrust upward atop newly
bulged continents and before these elevated surfaces
have been eroded away. The presence of perpetually
cold mountaintops, where thickening ice packs form
and flow down into the valleys, (Plate IV), is evidently needed to trigger the huge glaciation process.
We also know that the periodic fluctuations in global
temperature must be associated in a casual way with
fluctuations in the amount of solar radiation reaching
the earth's surface. But we can only theorize as to
what produces the latter, weighing as we do so such
factors as possible periodic changes in the amount
of radiant heat sent out by the sun, in the earthly
atmosphere, which solar radiation must penetrate,
and in the earth's rotation around the sun.

One highly ingenious theory, worked out by R. A.
Lyttleton and Hoyle, is presented by the latter in his
aforementioned *The Nature of the Universe*. He associates variations in the sun's radiance with the "fat-
ness" of the "tunnel" the sun bores through interstellar hydrogen gas. There are vast clouds of such gas
within our galaxy, as every professional stargazer
knows to his sorrow, since they blot from his tele-
scopic vision all but a fraction of our island universe.
Through these gas clouds the stars move at speeds
that vary relative to eddies and ripples in the gas,
and they pull hydrogen into themselves in quantities
that vary inversely with their speed. The lower the
relative speed, the higher the amount of gas sucked
in and the "fatter" the consequent tunnel. If the
speed is (relatively) very low—say, 5000 miles an
hour or less—the tunnel becomes a very fat one and
the amount of material sucked into the star becomes
sufficiently great to increase its size appreciably within
a few million years. At the present time, the sun's
speed relative to the gas through which it passes is

around 30,000 miles an hour, which is much too high to permit the boring of a large tunnel; the amount of hydrogen acquired by the sun in this way is not great enough, at the present rate, to increase its size appreciably in ten billion years. But there is no reason to assume that the sun has always had the same speed relative to the gas, nor that it will always have. On the contrary, it seems more than likely that at times in the past (as in times in the future) the relative speed has been (and will be) much lower than it now is and the tunnel therefore much fatter. During these times the sucked-in hydrogen must have significantly increased the sun's radiance. Why? Because this hydrogen falls upon the sun surface at speeds in excess of a million miles an hour; the impact produces very significant quantities of heat. This increase in the sun's heat means, of course, an increase in the earth's surface temperature. It would account for the fact that semi-tropical forests once grew in Spitzbergen (the coal found there is evidence of this) within 12 degrees of the North Pole.

It may also account, suggests Hoyle, for the incidence of ice ages. He refers to the curious opinion of some meteorologists that an *increase* rather than a *decrease* of solar heat is required to produce an ice age —though of course the increase must be considerably smaller, for this effect, than one permitting semi-tropical vegetation in Spitzbergen. The argument of these meteorologists is that a moderate increase in the earth's surface temperatures would bring an increase in cloudiness over the polar regions, which in turn would make for warmer winters (because of the high latent heats of the atmospheric water) and cooler summers (because the cloud's upper surface would reflect back into space major portions of the solar radiation which would otherwise fall upon the snow). The latter phenomenon—cooler summers—is deemed crucial to the accumulation of snow and ice because it prevents the melting which would otherwise occur. Hence the steady growth and flow of vast glaciers.

The theory gains further plausibility from the fact that the spread of snow and ice would, of itself alone, tend to reduce earthly temperatures. For one thing, the white glistening surfaces would reflect a significant proportion of the solar light and heat which the earth surface would otherwise absorb; a snow field is virtually opaque to solar beams striking it at a large incident angle (that is, an angle measured from a perpendicular drawn to the surface). For another thing, the locking up of vast quantities of water in perpetual ice and snow would reduce the amount of water in the oceans and hence their effectiveness as heat reservoirs that moderate the climate.

Nevertheless, the theory as a whole is unacceptable to most scientists concerned with problems of long-range climatic fluctuations. It founders, for these, on its major premise—to wit, that ice ages are inaugurated by temperature increases. Precisely the opposite is true, writes E. J. Öpik of the Armagh Observatory in Northern Ireland, speaking for most of his colleagues in support of the common-sense notion that widespread glaciation is the effect of a marked lowering of temperatures. "Snow can accumulate on the ground only when the temperature is near the freezing point," he says; "when the global temperature rises, the snow line shifts poleward, and the area of accumulation decreases. Over this area the degree of moisture remains practically constant, corresponding to the constant temperature of the snow line. The decreased area means decreased accumulation of snow and less favorable conditions for the formation of ice caps." Öpik suggests that long-range temperature fluctuations are associated with events occurring "in the normal course of evolution of a star like our Sun." At various times in the sun's life the conversion of hydrogen to helium in its deep interior must join with gas diffusion to "create zones of instability and mixing." While in this state of imbalance, the sun would radiate less heat and a glacial epoch would occur on earth, to be terminated only when solar equilibrium had been re-established. "This process is repeated after intervals of the order of several hundred million years, which explains the recurrence of glacial epochs."

But what causes the successive advances and recessions of ice—the successive ice ages—within the long glacial epochs? Perhaps a further knowledge of sunspots and the sunspot cycle will provide a clue.

Water as Energy Custodian

We have now to consider the vital role played by water as custodian and transporter of solar energy upon the earth. Over the earth as a whole water plays this role in all three states, solid, liquid, and gaseous, but chiefly in the latter two. As a vapor in the atmosphere, alternately condensing into droplets and evaporating again, it is a principal molder of climates and maker of the daily weather; as a liquid in seas and oceans, it operates as a global thermostat.

Consider, first, the ceaseless circulation of water—from ocean to air to soil to river to ocean again—which is known as the hydrologic (or water) cycle. (See Fig. 21.) Every year, about 80,000 cubic miles of water is evaporated from the oceans of the world. At the same time about 15,000 cubic miles is evaporated from lakes and rivers and land surfaces of the continents. Thus a total of approximately 95,000 cubic miles of water is wafted into the atmosphere to become a total precipitation of 95,000 cubic miles

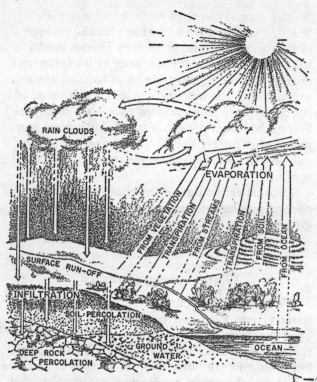

FIG. 21.   *The water cycle is a ceaseless circulation from ocean to air to soil to river to ocean, evaporating and precipitating about 95,000 cubic miles of water a year in the processes depicted here.*

each year, since in any year the process of evaporation is matched virtually pound for pound by the fall of water as rain or snow. Most of this precipitation goes directly into the ocean again, but some 24,000 cubic miles of it—enough to cover Texas to a depth of 475 feet—falls on land surfaces. Some of this precipitated water runs directly off the solid surfaces into streams and rivers, which carry it in a few days or weeks out to sea again; some of it is immediately evaporated back into the atmosphere; but much of it soaks into the soil where it performs vital plant-feeding functions, or deeper into subsoil and rock where it forms reservoirs and subterranean rivers, feeding back, swiftly or slowly, into surface springs and rivers and lakes.

Now when a gram of water is evaporated it absorbs nearly 600 calories of energy and may be pictured as lifting these, like so many bundles of dynamism, into the air. Here the dispersed water molecules often enter the world-wide circulatory system set up by an uneven distribution of the sun's radiant energy over the earth. More energy is received in equatorial regions than anywhere else on earth, and the amount of energy received diminishes progressively as one proceeds either to the north or south of this middle line. In the tropics, therefore, evaporation rates are higher and the air is warmer than elsewhere—and not only does more moisture enter the air but this moisture rises higher above the surface of tropical lands and seas. At high altitudes the warm moist air flows outward in generally northward and southward directions, gradually sinking toward the surface as it loses heat, and grows denser until it encounters an air mass from the polar regions.

While the tropical air is being heated and loaded with moisture, a very different sequence of events occurs in regions of high latitude. There, in the winter season, the slanting solar beam never strikes the earth's surface, which, radiating away energy, becomes very cold.

The air in contact with it likewise becomes frigidly cold and very dense. Because of the cold the air contains very few water molecules in comparison with the air in the tropics. After days, or weeks, of sitting still, gathering substance, the cold high-pressure system becomes unstable and starts to move ponderously toward lower latitudes. Soon the battle is joined between the two dissimilar masses of air: the cold, dense, dry arctic mass and the warm, moisture-laden tropical mass. As the arctic mass slips toward low latitudes, it hugs the earth's surface, pushing under the advancing warm air, and the warm air is thus forced again to rise in a region where temperatures are much lower than in the tropics, until the untold billions of water molecules evaporated from the tropical seas can no longer remain dispersed in gaseous form. They must condense into liquid, the condensation nuclei being minute particles of salt or dust, and each gram of water thus condensed releases some 600 calories of heat energy into the air. The addition of this heat energy transported to high latitudes by water, the energy custodian, is essential to the formation of low-pressure wave cyclones along the boundary surfaces between the cold and warm air masses—that is, along the cold fronts. The development of these wave cyclones becomes an integral part of the total complex system by which solar energy received in uneven amounts is redistributed over the earth's surface. Without such energy transfers a very small percentage of the world's land surfaces would be comfortably habitable by men—and the climate of most regions, because of an excess of heat or cold, would be unbearable.

But, as we have indicated, evaporated water caught up in atmospheric circulatory systems is by no means the sole transporter of stored heat. Water remaining liquid in the oceans is also vastly effective in moving solar energy over thousands of miles. Though direct evidence is difficult to come by, convection currents must operate to some extent in the oceans. The heated equatorial water must drift slowly toward the poles, while beneath them dense, cold polar water creeps along the ocean floor toward the tropics. Arrived in the warmer zone, this cold water must gradually rise to replace the surface water which has drifted away; as it rises into sunlight it is warmed. In general, we may say in passing, water is rather remarkably transparent (visible light can penetrate it to a depth of half a mile), though not equally transparent to the whole of the spectrum. Its blue-green color indicates that it is relatively opaque toward the infrared end of the spectrum—the end where light waves emerge into heat waves—and this, of course, affects water's capacity and nature as heat absorber and custodian.

The importance of ocean convection in heat transport is negligible, however, compared to that of the so-called "ocean rivers." These are distinct currents of warm and cold water powered by the mighty circulatory system of the air. There is no need here to go into a detailed technical description of how permanent high-pressure and low-pressure areas are created over portions of the globe, how prevailing winds are generated by a combination of convection and earthly rotation, and how all these effect a heaping up of ocean waters in some areas and a pressing down of them in others and a shoving of some of them into great surface streams, which are far more permanent in location, and constant in volume, than are the rivers that flow between banks of rock and soil upon the continents. Virtually every one of the continental rivers has changed its course and drastically modified its character within recorded history, but the rivers of the ocean remain essentially as they have been for many scores of thousands of years. Figure 22 maps the principal ocean currents, of which the warm ones, carrying tropical waters into colder climes, are the Gulf Stream, the Japan Current, the Brazilian Current, and Australian Current. The counterparts of these, cold currents bringing arctic waters into warmer climes, are the Canary Current, the Califor-

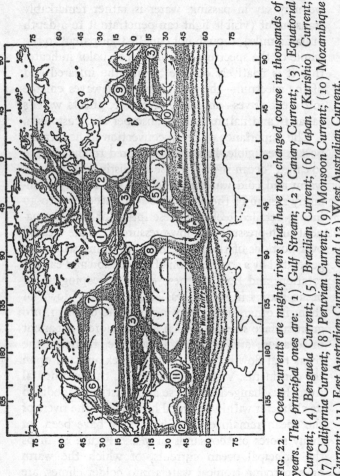

FIG. 22.   Ocean currents are mighty rivers that have not changed course in thousands of years. The principal ones are: (1) Gulf Stream; (2) Canary Current; (3) Equatorial Current; (4) Benguela Current; (5) Brazilian Current; (6) Japan (Kurishio) Current; (7) California Current; (8) Peruvian Current; (9) Monsoon Current; (10) Mozambique Current; (11) East Australian Current, and (12) West Australian Current.

nia Current, the Peruvian Current (sometimes called the Humboldt), and the Benguela Current.

The Gulf Stream, which is of major importance to northwestern Europe and southeastern United States, may be cited as example. It is said to "rise" off Florida because, quite literally, due to pressure variations set up there in the ocean, its warm water does come up at this point from lower depths. Off Florida, the Gulf Stream's flow at a depth of 800 feet is around two and one half miles an hour; at the surface the flow is sometimes nearly six miles an hour. These speeds are high compared with those of ocean currents in general. Since the Gulf Stream is approximately fifty miles wide at the point where those measurements have been made, its total flow there amounts to very nearly 100 cubic miles of water per hour—equivalent to some twenty-five times the total drainage of all the major rivers of all the continents. The Stream's temperature in the region of its rising is in the 80s Fahrenheit, and though it grows cooler as it flows northeast, it remains warm enough to raise temperatures in Norway some 20 to 25 degrees above the expected for those latitudes. It is because of the Gulf Stream that the climate of the British Isles is temperate whereas that of Labrador, which is in the same latitude, is frigid. The latter land is washed by the Gulf Stream's opposite number, the Labrador Current, which brings cold water and occasional icebergs down from the Arctic.

CHAPTER 6

The Waters of Life

The Days of Creation

A few years ago, when many scientists were inclined to accept Sir James Jeans's theory of earthly creation, the possibility that life like our own existed in other parts of the universe was considered remote. It has been calculated that only once, on the average, in 500 billion years would one star come close enough to another to produce a tidal outsurge of matter which could be torn away in the manner envisaged by Jeans. Even if we assumed that the average age of stars was considerably greater than ten billion years —and we now assume lesser age for the stars in our galaxy—fewer than one out of fifty million of them could have collided or nearly collided with another in the whole of their lives. Of these exceedingly rare near misses only a very small fraction—one out of thousands—would actually produce planetary systems, and the chance that any of these would include an earthlike body, where the conditions necessary for life prevailed, was surely not more than one in several hundred. "Our solar system appears, therefore, to be a system that is nearly, though perhaps not quite, unique in our stellar universe," wrote H. Spencer Jones in the late 1930s.[1]

[1] *Life on Other Worlds* (Macmillan, 1940).

But with the rejection of the Jeans hypothesis of creation and the acceptance of any of the four we described in the preceding chapter, the situation is reversed. If we accept Hoyle's theory that our sun acquired a planetary system in the explosion of a companion star approximately one light-hour away, the chances are (in Hoyle's words) "that rather more than a million stars in the Milky Way possess planets on which you might live without undue discomfort." If we accept the theory that stars were formed out of cold interstellar clouds of gas (protostars), we must conclude that several out of each one hundred stars have histories closely similar to the sun's. Since there are some 100 billion stars in our galaxy, there must be (by this theory) several billions of planetary systems and many millions of worlds like the earth. If we accept the Weizsäcker conception of planetary formation, as Gamow does, we must conclude that virtually every star possesses a planetary system and that there are at least scores of millions, and probably hundreds of millions, of planets in the Milky Way where physical conditions are practically identical with those on earth. The same is true if we accept Alfvén's theory, whereby the formation of planets is explained in terms of the behavior of ionized gases in a magnetic field. All stars, by this theory, should have a retinue of planets, and every star having the same mass as our sun should have, as the third planet out from it, a body closely similar to the earth in all respects. "And it would be at least strange," writes Gamow, "if life—even in its highest forms—had failed to develop in these 'inhabitable' worlds."[2]

Scientists now quite generally believe that such life has developed—that when we look up into the night

[2] *One Two Three . . . Infinity* (Mentor Books, New American Library, 1953), page 294.

sky we may see, even with our naked eyes, several stars that shine as suns upon planets like our own. We cannot see the planets themselves; shining as they do with only a reflected light, they are much too far away to be visible through even the most powerful telescope. But it seems to many scientists distinctly possible, even probable, that we on earth will some-day be able to exchange messages with creatures on other worlds whose intelligence and technology match or surpass our own. Indeed, only recently, as this is written, a project (Project Ozma) was initi-ated at the National Radio Astronomy Observatory to search with large radio telescopes for possible "pulse code" radio signals broadcast into interstellar space by other-worldly minds.

Of one thing we may be almost certain: such life as exists on earthlike planets elsewhere in the uni-verse must be, in essence, similar to life on earth. It may have taken forms different from any living things we know, but in its substantial nature it must have derived very largely, as earthly life has done, from the operations of two vital chemical entities— water and carbon dioxide—and it must have done so according to the same universal laws of physics and chemistry. True, some scientists have theorized that silicon in other worlds may have played the role as-signed carbon on earth and that the results may be so radically different from the life we know as to be ut-terly alien to us. Like carbon, silicon has the ability to build up large and complex molecules that are very delicately balanced—an ability necessary to the de-velopment of living stuff. However, its ability in this direction is much more limited than carbon's, so that the chances seem overwhelmingly against its ever winning out over the latter element, on an earthlike planet, in the realization of vital possibilities.

Even in the forms it assumes, this other-worldly

life (if it exists) is very probably similar to life on earth. The formal possibilities, after all, are not unlimited and a fair proportion of them must be realized in the almost incredibly rich variety of the life forms on our planet. Moreover, the same processes of natural selection that operate in the evolution of living forms on earth should operate in any similar environment toward analogous if not precisely similar ends over the same length of time. "There are such great advantages to walking on two legs, in carrying one's brain in one's head, in having two eyes on the same eminence at a height of five or six feet," writes biologist C. D. Darlington, "that we might as well take quite seriously the possibility of a pseudo man and a pseudo woman with some physical resemblance to ourselves."

It follows that our very general description of how life began may apply quite as well to other worlds as it does to our own. There, as here, the atmosphere must at one time have consisted largely of water vapor and carbon dioxide. There, as here, enormous and prolonged rainstorms must have fallen for centuries, gradually filling up the ocean basins as the planet's crust cooled. And there, as here, life may well have begun in warm and shallow seas as the cloud mantle tore apart to let the sun shine through. Certainly the conditions essential to the existence of life were present in such seas on earth, and present in such a balance of light, temperature, salt concentration, atmospheric pressure, and gaseous solution as has never since been duplicated on earth, save (to a very limited degree) in scientific laboratories. Mineral salts, washed down from the land surfaces, were present. Carbon dioxide was present, dissolved in water and combined with it to form carbonic acid (H_2CO_3). And ultraviolet light was present in an abundance that no longer occurs on earth: the atmosphere of those days, being empty of free oxygen, was much more penetrable by ultraviolet waves than is the atmosphere of today.

Now laboratory experiments have demonstrated that if sufficient ultraviolet light falls upon water mixtures of carbon dioxide and ammonia at warm temperatures, primitive photosynthesis (that is, the making of carbohydrates out of water and carbon dioxide in the presence of light) can occur even in the absence of chlorophyll (the green stuff with which plants achieve photosynthesis)—and that other simple organic (or carbon) compounds, including some with nitrogen, can be synthesized, too. This strongly suggests that a manufacture of organic matter, similar to that of the laboratory but on an immensely vaster scale, went on in the primeval oceans until, in the absence of bacteria or any other living substance to consume it, this organic stuff had transformed sea water into a substance with "the consistency of hot soup," to quote J. B. S. Haldane. From this broth, so rich in stored energy from the sun, so beautifully adapted to the feeding of living things, life itself remained for a long time absent. But all through this time the peculiar properties of water, actively manifested, were involved with manifestations of the distinctive chemical properties of carbon in the building up of larger, ever more complex molecules.

The Seedbeds of Life

We have sufficiently dilated upon the properties of water to indicate the ways in which this unusual substance in its liquid state would facilitate the building up of complicated molecular structures. Suffice it to add that insofar as it actually joins in the formation of chemical compounds, it does so through a dissolution, not just of the hydrogen bonds holding water molecules together, but of the chemical bonds which hold together the constituent H^+ ions and OH^- ions. The ions become, in the process, constituents of the built-up substance. As for carbon, what makes it uniquely valuable as the building material of life is its capacity to serve as a chain linking together huge aggregations of atoms in single molecules. The organic chemist (organic chemistry, as you may know, is the chemistry of carbon compounds) is constantly concerned with molecules made up of several times as many atoms as are contained in the molecules with which the inorganic chemist is concerned, except when the latter deals with silica compounds. Typical chemical formulae for inorganic compounds describe molecules of from two to eight or ten atoms: $NaCl$ (two atoms), K_2SO_4 (seven atoms), $Pb (NO_3)_2$ (nine atoms). Typical formulae of organic compounds are $C_3H_5 (NO_3)_3$ (twenty atoms), $C_{12}H_{22}O_{11}$ (forty-five atoms), and $C_{40}H_{56}$ (ninety-six atoms).

This unique combining capacity of carbon is commonly expressed in scientific language by saying that the carbon atom is tetravalent. You may recall that in Chapter 3 we mentioned *valence*, or "combining power," as we described how elemental atoms are joined together in molecules through a sharing of electrons in their outer, or valence, shells, the tendency being always toward the stable electronic structure of an inert gas. Valence has a numerical value in terms of hydrogen. Thus the gas chlorine is said to be monovalent—to have, in other words, a valence of one—because a single atom of it combines with a single atom of hydrogen to produce a molecule of HCl, or hydrochloric acid. Oxygen is said to be divalent (or to have a valence of two) because a single atom of it combines with two atoms of hydrogen to make H_2O. Nitrogen is trivalent, meaning that three atoms of hydrogen combine with it to produce ammonia,

NH_3. And carbon, as we have said, is tetravalent. It combines with four atoms of hydrogen to produce the poisonous gas methane, CH_4.

You can readily see how the assignment of a numerical valence to any element involves the indirect assignment of it to any other element with which the first combines in a one-to-one ratio. For example, to say that chlorine is monovalent is tantamount to saying that sodium is, too, since one sodium atom and one chlorine atom combine to form a molecule of common table salt, or NaCl. To say that oxygen is divalent is to say that calcium also is, since one atom of calcium combines with one of oxygen to make calcium oxide, CaO. You can also readily see that the higher an element's valence, the greater should be the possible complexity of the atomic combinations it can (so to speak) organize. Each valence is an arm by which an atom may link itself to other atoms; the more arms, the more linkages possible. Monovalent atoms are so severely limited in combining power that they cannot be the central organizers of a large group of atoms. With monovalent sodium, monovalent chlorine can form one and only one compound, for when the two are linked arm in arm as table salt, there is no arm left free to link with another atom. Divalent oxygen has a greater freedom of combining action. An atom of it may combine with one atom of another divalent element, as in calcium oxide (CaO), or with two atoms of a monovalent element, as in water (H_2O), or with one atom each of two different monovalent elements, as in caustic potash of potassium hydroxide (KOH). Much greater than oxygen's power to link up complex molecules is that of trivalent elements, and the maximum power in this respect is reached with tetravalent elements, especially (for complex reasons we need not explore here) with carbon.

We should perhaps add that there are elements which are pentavalent (five-valenced) in a few of their chemical relationships, but only in a few. Most of the time two of their valences are shaking hands with each other, if one may thus extend the metaphor, and so are unable to grasp the arms of other atoms. In other words, they operate in general as trivalent elements. Nitrogen, for instance, is occasionally pentavalent but generally trivalent, as in the example of ammonia.

The carbon atom may employ its four valence arms in two ways. It may link all four arms with other atoms, in which case it is said to be *saturated*; it may, on the other hand, join two of its four arms to each other and employ only the other two as linkages with other atoms, in which case it is described as *unsaturated*. In carbon monoxide (CO), the carbon atom is unsaturated, two unattached arms being entangled with each other. In methane (CH_4)—believed to have been an important constituent of that earliest earth atmosphere lost into outer space—the carbon atom is saturated, the molecule being diagramed as follows:

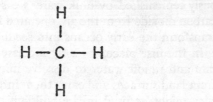

Methane is the simplest of what are called hydrocarbons—compounds containing only carbon and hydrogen atoms—and hydrocarbons in turn are the simplest of all organic compounds. Even so, they are sometimes molecules of enormous size and very considerable complexity. Take, for example, the hydrocarbon $C_{40}H_{56}$. This is the red coloring matter of tomatoes, called lycopene; the central theme of its un-saturated molecule is a chain of alternately single- and double-bonded carbon atoms. In the primeval oceans, among the earliest of organic compounds to be built up out of carbon and water and sunlight may have been the simplest of sugars, whose molecule has as its structural base a chain of six carbon atoms to which are hooked hydrogen ions (H^+), hydroxyl ions (OH^-), and an atom of oxygen (O), as follows:

$$H-\underset{\underset{\displaystyle OH}{|}}{\overset{\overset{\displaystyle H}{|}}{C}}-\underset{\underset{\displaystyle OH}{|}}{\overset{\overset{\displaystyle H}{|}}{C}}-\underset{\underset{\displaystyle OH}{|}}{\overset{\overset{\displaystyle H}{|}}{C}}-\underset{\underset{\displaystyle OH}{|}}{\overset{\overset{\displaystyle H}{|}}{C}}-\underset{\underset{\displaystyle OH}{|}}{\overset{\overset{\displaystyle H}{|}}{C}}-\underset{\underset{\displaystyle OH}{|}}{\overset{\overset{\displaystyle H}{|}}{C}}=O$$

Much more complex, perhaps too complex to have been developed at all in oceans empty as yet of plant and animal life, are the very simplest of fats and proteins, which, with carbohydrates (sugars and starches), make up the three general classes of organic substance produced by plants and animals.

Now carbonic acid, washed out of the primitive atmosphere as torrential rains came down, continuously replenished by bulk water's easy absorption of carbon dioxide from the air, operated in three ways to transform the early oceans into seedbeds of life.

In the first place, it vastly increased the ability of rain and runoff water to dissolve mineral substances from land surfaces and carry them into the sea, where they might be used in the build-up of living bodies. Most minerals dissolve to a slight degree in pure water, but in water that is saturated with carbonic acid the rate of solution is vastly increased. Hence this all-pervasive acid is of enormous geologic importance; it accounts for much of the speed with which rocks are weathered and minerals leached from the soil. "Indeed," writes Lawrence J. Henderson in his *The*

Fitness of the Environment, "it is the united action of water and carbonic acid . . . which sets free the inorganic constituents of the Earth's crust and turns them into the stream of metabolism." ("Metabolism" is the scientific term for the physical processes of life, the building up and tearing down of living tissues.)

In the second place, carbonic acid has certain unique properties which largely accounted for the neutrality or very faint alkalinity of even the earliest oceans. This was a condition necessary for the development of the essential substance of life, called protoplasm, and a condition which would be duplicated (again largely in consequence of carbonic acid) *in* protoplasm. But what do we mean by "acid"? What by "alkaline"? And what by "neutral" as applied to solutions? In chemical terminology an *acid* is a hydrogen-containing substance which, when dissolved in water, sets hydrogen ions (H^+) free, increasing the number or concentration of such ions per unit volume of the solution. An *alkaline,* or *base* as it is often called, is a substance containing oxygen and hydrogen atoms linked as a group, called hydroxides, which dissociates upon solution in water to increase the hydroxyl ion (OH^-) concentration. When the numbers of hydrogen and hydroxyl ions in a solution are equal or very nearly so, the solution is said to be *neutral.* A "strong" acid or base is one whose molecules readily split apart in water to yield a high concentration of hydrogen or hydroxyl ions; in dilute solutions—that is, solutions where the amount of water in proportion to the amount of dissolved substance (solute) is very high—the ionization of strong acids or bases is complete. It should be evident from this that strong acids and bases, when placed in the same dilute solution, will neutralize each other completely, the neutralization reaction being precisely that by which water is formed through a union of the hydrogen ion with the hydroxyl ion:

$$H^+ + OH^- \rightleftharpoons H_2O*$$

It should also be evident that only in solutions that are neutral or practically so—solutions wherein the solvent is chemically inert—are complex organic combinations possible. In solutions strongly acid or alkaline, the tolerance needed for a wide range of delicately balanced bonding arrangements is lost.

Of literally vital importance, then, is the fact that carbonic acid (H_2CO_3) is a weak acid whose unique property is that it preserves a *neutral* reaction whenever it is in solution with its salts (such as calcium carbonate, $CaCO_3$, the primary stuff of shells and bones), provided that it is present in excess of the amount used up in salt-producing reactions, as, of course, it always is in the sea. No acid even slightly stronger or weaker than carbonic acid has this property, whose importance in maintaining the near-perfect neutrality of the oceans wherein life was made, and of the protoplasm and blood of the life that evolved, is impossible to overestimate.

In the third place, carbonic acid provided most of the vital seed which would grow in the ocean seedbeds it had done so much to prepare, for from it came most of the carbon atoms, whose unique combining

* Water itself, you may recall from Chapter 3, is very slightly ionized, so slightly as to make it a very poor conductor of electricity. The hydrogen-ion concentration of pure water is about 1×10^{-7}. We therefore say that the *p*H of water is 7, *p*H being the negative common logarithm of the hydrogen-ion concentration. (We'll have to assume here that you've had enough mathematics to know what logarithms are.) The concentration of hydroxyl ions in pure water is also 1×10^{-7}, which is to say that water is neither acid nor base but neutral. Any neutral solution, then, is one having a *p*H of 7. If the *p*H is greater than 7, the solution is alkaline; if it is less than 7, the solution is acid.

powers were the necessary condition of complex atomic organization.

As these carbon atoms were linked together in long and branching stems, to which were hooked hydrogen and nitrogen—as they coiled into spirals and loops—they structured molecules so huge and feebly stable that they constantly were on the verge of falling apart. Such entities could maintain themselves, it would seem, only through effort: they had to employ a certain kind of energy, inwardly directed in unprecedented ways, and this effort, this energy, was life. No doubt there are philosophical implications here, implications highly critical of the view that the best society is a perfectly balanced order and that the proper aim of education is the thoroughly "well-adjusted" or perfectly balanced mind and personality. Such a view, if pressed very far in action, would appear on scientific grounds to be anti-vital. Life arises out of a state of instability and imbalance; its earliest manifestation is a rudimentary irritability; and it has as its very essence a perpetual striving to maintain itself, a perpetual reaching out and falling forward as it makes its precarious way against the death outside and the death within. For life does have death in its very heart. Living involves dying and, in one sense, actually consists of dying, just as dying consists of living to the extent that the very substance of death must be a substance that lives. Only by a slender margin, and only for a little while, do the processes of organic construction (anabolism) outpace the processes of organic disintegration (catabolism) in the vital race we call metabolism. And if we incline to despair because catabolism seems to win this race in the end, we do well to remember that without it there would be no race at all.

Was the transition from dead to living matter achieved abruptly in the primeval oceans? Or did it come about through a slow, gradual evolution wherein it would be almost impossible to mark the point in time of its beginning or the form of its first occurrence? No one knows for sure. We do know that in the microscopic world at the present time there exist forms of matter of which it is almost impossible to say whether or not they are alive. They exist in a kind of limbo between the living and the dead, having some of the properties we associate with life but lacking others we consider indispensable to life. For instance, there exist molecular viruses (nucleoproteins) which, when injected into certain kinds of living cells, will reproduce themselves. But they cannot reproduce in a non-vital medium. Are they alive or dead? And it is perhaps not irrelevant to this whole question to point out that even wholly inorganic structures may display, under certain conditions, two properties we normally associate only with living matter: they are capable of growth, and they react to the stimulus of light (that is, they exhibit the phenomenon known as phototropism).

Quite probably, then, carbon compounds in the primeval oceans grew in molecular size and complexity until some of them reached an unstable form in which they were chemically self-reproductive. Any such form, said H. G. Wells and Julian Huxley in *The Science of Life*, "would have found in this soupy sea abundant food and stores of potential energy to support it, while it (or rather, no doubt, one survivor among a host of descendant streams, most of them unsuccessful) evolved into something really alive."

But what characterizes "something really alive"? Its over-all characteristic is that it is self-defining, self-determining, self-reproductive. Non-living bodies often seem to possess one or two of the peculiarities of life, as we have pointed out, but never are these peculiarities the manifestation of an inward, self-directed force. When a non-living substance turns toward light, it is responding to a purely external stimulus and doing so (in a manner of speaking) from the outside; a living substance, particularly in its simplest forms, may do the same, but in other forms it actively *seeks* light, proceeding from the inside out. When a non-living substance grows, it grows from the outside only, through accretion, or external addition. A living substance, on the other hand, grows through the inward absorption of food and the organization of it, from the inside out, as vital tissue. A non-living substance has no characteristic size and shape by which it may be defined: these are imposed in any given case by external conditions. Water may exist as a wisp of vapor or as an ocean—and though any body of water has a definite shape, this is the shape of the containing basin and is not characteristic of the water itself. A living body, on the other hand, has a characteristic size toward which it is urged by inner forces of growth and beyond which it does not grow, and it has a characteristic shape by which its kind of being may be distinguished from all other kinds. There are yet other vital properties, some of which we have mentioned: reproductiveness; a functioning metabolism; irritability, or reactiveness; a definite organization into cells (the primitive forms are unicellular, or one-celled); an inner-directed mobility; and a definite chemical composition which is distinct from that of any non-living stuff. This chemical composition is, of course, protoplasm—the "physical basis of life," as T. H. Huxley put it—and though the proportion of the elements it contains varies widely among the different kinds of life, over 50 per cent of it always is water.

Water and Life

At some time very long ago, then, in warm and shallow and food-rich seas, indubitably living matter was produced, matter embodying a wholly new kind of energy on earth in that it was in part (and in increasing part as evolution proceeded) self-directive. Perhaps we may accurately picture it as a kind of slime which branched and divided and assumed myriad sizes and shapes and chemical compositions as it reached out, gropingly, yearningly, for food and stability. At first this slime probably consisted of single-celled creatures, each cell being a small mass of protoplasm containing a tiny dense body known as the nucleus. Later the cells were joined together and modified in different ways, or modified themselves, while remaining a part of the community, in order to perform different, specialized functions. Thus were complex and ever more complex organisms developed.

Very early in the evolutionary process, a part of this sea slime became green. It became colored with that wonderful pigment known as chlorophyll, which can utilize the radiant energy of light to make complex foods out of carbon dioxide and water—food used both as vital energy and as the building material of bodies. Other portions of the slime, lacking chlorophyll, became dependent for their food ultimately upon substances possessing chlorophyll. They thus began their evolution under an initial disadvantage, being vitally subordinate to other forms, but as their evolution proceeded they gained in mobility and consequent freedom of choice (the essence of consciousness) far more than they lost in absolute food security from the lack of chlorophyll of their own. Thus were separated the animal and vegetable kingdoms, divergent streams of evolution having a common source but very different ends. Eventually, then, life emerged in myriad forms from the sea onto dry land—as vegetable matter first of all, probably, but very closely followed by living forms feeding on vegetable matter or on one another or on both. The latter were life forms that need no longer depend upon an external fluid— a near-neutral salty solution of organic compounds— for their food supply or for carrying away the toxic wastes of their metabolism. Instead, their tissues were bathed by an internal salty fluid; as we suggested in Chapter 1, they had managed to *internalize* sea water, so to speak, by transforming it into blood. Moreover, there was developed by then a wonderful balancing of the waste products of plants against the waste products of animals. Of the former, the wastes consisted of oxygen in large proportion, carbon dioxide in smaller proportion, and water; of the latter, the wastes consisted of carbon dioxide, water, urea, and feces—and of no oxygen at all. Thus the gaseous wastes of the vegetable kingdom became the gaseous food of the animal, and vice versa, the plants using up the carbon dioxide breathed out by animals as the animals used the oxygen breathed out by plants.

The story of how this branched stream of life multiplied its shapes and kinds—of how rudimentary irritability became consciousness and consciousness became an increasingly abstract and complex intellectuality—is no proper part of our essay. We need only say that in every phase of this evolutionary process, water with its remarkable properties played a leading and sometimes a dominant role, and that the evolving life increasingly modified its environment, which is to say that the waters of life did also.

One modification was of the earth's surface, whose harsh mineral contours were in general softened and whose colors were made more richly various by the operations of plant and animal life. In the seas were shelled creatures and fish whose dead bodies rained down continually upon the ocean floor to form deposits of limestone; these became part of the exposed land surface as the earth crust crinkled and heaved, and the seas were shifted about. On land, the chemistry of primitive vegetable matter and later the roots of plants greatly aided the wind and rain in the weathering of rocks and the manufacture of soil.

Another modification, a very important one, was of the atmosphere. As millions of years passed, vegetable matter dying in the soil formed immense deposits of carbon in the form of coal and oil and peat. By these deposits, and by the expiration of oxygen by plants, carbon dioxide was gradually removed from the atmosphere and oxygen substituted for it. At the present time carbon dioxide, which once made up a major portion of the atmosphere, constitutes only a little more than 0.03 per cent of it by volume. This change in the composition of the atmosphere has, of course, had effects upon the earth's climate.

Man's Water Problems

But by far the greatest modification by life of its environment has been consciously effected as man has developed his technology, his civilization. It is a modification which has produced, in recent years, increasingly acute water problems.

You will recall that in our introduction we spoke of the "usualness," in one sense, of this substance which, in terms of physical chemistry, is so unusual. But we went on to say that even in the ordinary meaning of "usual" as a synonym for "commonplace," water becomes year by year a little more unusual. As man's numbers increase and his technology advances, he uses more and more water. In ancient times, when the world population was but a fraction of what it now is, the average person used from three to five gallons of water daily, and he did not use more than that, probably, in medieval times. In the nineteenth century, in the Western nations where technology was developed, the water consumption per capita increased to approximately ten to fifteen gallons daily. Since 1900, both the population and the per capita consumption have made enormous leaps. In the United States the population has doubled—and the per capita consumption of water has sextupled, what with our automatic washers, driers, dishwashers, air-conditioning systems, garbage disposals, and so on.

Irrigation in America uses about 100 billion gallons of water a day, while industry uses 70 billion gallons. To produce a bushel of corn requires 10 to 20 tons of water. Between 15 and 20 tons are required to produce a pound of beef. It requires 18 barrels of water to refine one barrel of oil, 300 gallons of water to produce one barrel of beer, 10 gallons of water to refine a gallon of gasoline, 250 tons of water to produce a ton of wood pulp, and 1000 tons of water to convert a ton of coal into electricity in a steam power plant. All in all, America now uses more than 240 billion gallons of water daily as compared with 40 billion sixty years ago, and it has been estimated by the U. S. Geological Survey that within twenty years the total U.S. consumption will reach 600 billion gallons daily!

Much of this water can be used over and over again, of course, but a significant portion of it cannot be; it is used up as steam or polluted with waste materials. There is a consequent steady lowering of the ground water table, requiring deeper and deeper wells, and the pollution of lakes and rivers by sewage and industrial wastes becomes every year a more serious problem and one more expensive to solve. Increasingly, it has become necessary in urban areas to sacrifice water quality to water quantity.

At the present time, there are two main lines of attack upon the problems of water shortage. One involves improvements in water economy—improvements, that is, in pollution prevention and removal and in the efficiency with which available supplies are used. The other involves the radical increase of available water supplies through rain making and through the conversion of sea water into fresh water.

A few years ago, one of the authors of this book made a study of water pollution in the Kansas River Basin, where he then lived. He examined the two-front attack being made on the problem there. On one front, the attack aims at cleaning up polluted waters so that they are again usable; on the other, the aim is to prevent pollution in the first place; and since both are typical of the country as a whole, we may use them here as examples.

Consider the manner in which Lawrence, Kansas, obtains a safe water supply for some 20,000 people. Two thirds of it comes from the Kansas River, one third from wells. In a treatment plant, this water is first partially sterilized with chlorine; pre-chlorination, this is called, because it takes place prior to the main treatment. Then the water is treated with alum, iron, and lime for flocculation, alum (as aluminum sulfate) reacting with lime to form aluminum hydroxide, iron sulfate reacting with lime to form iron hydroxide. The flocculent thus produced sweeps like an extremely fine-toothed comb through the water, cleaning out suspended materials. The water then pours into settling basins, where solids settle out, after which it flows through a succession of filters. These are layers of sand of a specified size, 36 inches thick. The water is then "softened" by treatment with lime and soda ash—which takes out such substances as calcium, magnesium, iron, and manganese—after which bicarbonate (having an acid reaction) is used to reduce the softener-induced alkalinity. The water is finally chlorinated again (post-chlorination) and pumped into the pipes of the Lawrence water system. Every other day each filter is cleaned by a process called "backwashing." The filter tank is emptied, water is forced through the sand from the bottom, and the accumulated filth of forty-eight hours boils up in liquid clouds to be flushed away by powerful streams of clean water. In this way the Lawrence plant treats some 3,000,000 gallons of water daily, or about 2000 gallons per minute.

As for the prevention of water pollution, it focuses largely on sewage treatment. The U. S. Public Health Service insists *that no sewage whatever should be dumped raw into a stream, that all should be treated before being thus disposed of.* The degree of needed treatment varies, however, with the amount and kind of sewage and the quantity and quality of water in the river. Sometimes "primary" treatment is sufficient, taken in conjunction with the stream's natural digestive capacities. Sometimes "secondary" treatment is also necessary.

"Primary" treatment is as simple as can be. Merely running the sewage water through a fine screen will reduce the amount of suspended solids by 20 to 25 per cent, the number of bacteria by 10 to 20 per cent, and the oxygen demand by 5 to 10 per cent. We should explain that organic pollution of water may be measured in terms of biochemical oxygen demand —or B.O.D., as it is called—this being the amount of oxygen required to oxidize the unstable organic compounds that are present: the higher the oxygen demand, the greater the pollution. If to screening is added a sedimentation process, whereby the sewage water is held in settling basins for a specified length of time, from 40 to 70 per cent of the suspended solids is removed, the bacterial count is reduced anywhere from 25 to 75 per cent, and the oxygen demand is cut by 25 to 40 per cent. These two processes of screening and sedimentation constitute "primary" treatment.

Of "secondary" treatments—and some such treatment is needed where the proportion of sewage to river volume is high—there are two main kinds.

The more complex of the two is the "activated sludge" process, whereby partially digested sewage solids, properly "activated" with bacteria, are used to speed the digestion of new, raw sewage. The basic operations are three: First, the sewage, after passing through screens and settling tanks, is mixed with from 20 to 35 per cent of its volume of biologically active sludge. Second, the mixture is agitated with air, which is forced through it and in the presence of which the bacterial digesters multiply rapidly; organic solids are swiftly oxidized and suspended materials tend to coagulate in forms that readily settle. Third, this final settlement takes place in special tanks. The water flowing out at the end of this process—the "effluent," as it is called—is clear and sparkling and contains very little organic material.

The other main secondary treatment is the "trickling filter" process, so named because its principal element is the trickling of sewage water over and through a six-to-eight-foot-deep bed of broken stones, each of which is two to four inches thick. A great advantage of this process, one which recommends it highly to small communities, is its simplicity. No considerable technical knowledge is required for its comprehension, and its operation requires little skill. The process, indeed, is virtually automatic.

Take the Smith Center, Kansas, plant for example. The sewage water enters this plant through a screen separating out the coarser solids and flows thence into a settling basin called an Imhoff tank, after the German, Karl Imhoff, who invented it. The tank is designed in such a way that gas bubbles from digesting solids at its bottom will not agitate the raw sewage above sufficiently to interfere with further settling. The tank stands several feet above the circular filtering bed. This enables a siphon arrangement at the exit trough to operate a rotary distributor turning above the bed. Through it, the sewage water (which has now had primary treatment) is sprayed over the coarse stones. From the filter bottom, through an underdrain system, the sewage water goes into the final settling tank, from which the sludge—a black tarlike substance—is obtained. This sludge may then be thrown back into the Imhoff tank for digestion or it may be put into a special digestion tank. Again, the effluent is clear, sparkling water containing very small amounts of organic material.

Activated-sludge plants, properly operated, will reduce the oxygen demand by 85 to 95 per cent, the suspended solids by the same proportion, and will remove from 90 to 98 per cent of all bacteria. Trickling-filter plants are only slightly less effective. They reduce oxygen demand by 80 to 95 per cent, suspended solids by 70 to 92 per cent, and bacteria by 90 to 95 per cent.

But the prevention of pollution is not the sole value which may be obtained from these treatment processes. The fermentation of sludge in a digestion tank yields a highly combustible gas or mixture of gases (methane makes up a large part of it) which may be piped away and used to operate plant machinery. In some cities considerable areas are lighted with electricity produced by generators whose fuel is sewer gas. Moreover, the sewage sludge left after complete digestion constitutes a humus immensely rich in plant food, and sludge is even richer in nitrates if digestion is not carried to its ultimate end—as it need not be. There exists in all the world no better substance for revivifying an exhausted soil, and it is a clean substance, which, unlike barnyard manure, may be pleasantly as well as safely handled. A few cities—not enough—pay substantial portions of their sewage-treatment costs by marketing the treatment's end product. "Milorganite" is the trade name for the fertilizer (fortified sewage sludge) produced by Milwaukee, Wisconsin, and "Soiltone" is the trade name for the dry, pulverized, digested sludge obtained from the Lincoln, Nebraska, and Des Moines, Iowa, plants.

But, as we have indicated, improvements in man's water economy by prevention and removal of pollution and in the efficiency with which available supplies are used have by no means solved the over-all problem of water shortage. The shortage grows more acute year by year. Hence the great emphasis now being given to experiments in rain making and in the conversion of sea water into fresh water.

It has been demonstrated that, under certain conditions, the "seeding" of clouds with fine particles of dry ice or silver iodide will induce precipitation, the grains serving as freezing nuclei for ice crystals of water which would otherwise remain in dispersed vapor form. Whether or not this device can be used on a sufficient scale to become important in our total water economy remains to be seen. Rain making is as yet in the experimental stage, and there is much controversy among scientists over the interpretation of experimental results. Even if it proves to be practical on scientific grounds, it may well prove impracticable on social and economic grounds. Who is to decide when and where and how much rain shall fall? And what criteria should be used?

As for the conversion of sea water into fresh water,

an effective way has, of course, been known for many centuries. It is distillation—that is, the boiling of water and the condensation of the resultant steam. This process, from this book's point of view, may be regarded as one of breaking the bonds between salt ions and water's polar molecules—the dehydration of hydrated ions, in other words—and in recent years several other methods of accomplishing this have been developed. All, however, have in the past been too expensive to be practical on any large scale. Until just a year or two ago, as this is written, the cost of sea-water conversion by the cheapest known process was around $4 per 1000 gallons of pure water produced, as compared with a U.S. average of 30 cents per 1000 gallons of tap water drawn from wells, lakes, and rivers.

In early 1960 officials of the U. S. Department of the Interior, the governmental agency officially concerned with water problems, let it be known that a distillation process had been developed, and was about to undergo pilot-project tests on a large scale, to convert salt water into fresh water at an estimated cost of less than $1 per 1000 gallons. A number of years ago scientists and engineers developed a method of running sea water into hot pipes, where it was vaporized, the vapor being then drawn off into cold pipes, where it condensed into pure water. The trouble with this method was that salt, precipitated out of the sea water as the latter boiled, formed a scale upon pipe walls, clogging them rapidly. The rate of clogging was reduced when pipes of expensive copper-nickel alloy were used instead of steel or lead, but it continued high enough to make the method far too costly for big operations. Then, sometime in 1958, a Michigan chemical engineer named Walter L. Badger attacked the problem with an idea remarkably similar, essentially, to artificial rain making. Obviously, salt crystals in sea water had an attraction for each other: they tended to stick together as the amount of liquid water in which they were originally dissolved or suspended was diminished by vaporization. This property of the salts accelerated the rate of scale formation on pipe walls as distillation proceeded. Since this was so, why not introduce pellets of broken-up scale into the original sea water as it was poured into the pipes? Wouldn't the pellets in that case serve as condensation nuclei whereby salt that would otherwise be deposited on metal would shape into "drops" that remained suspended in the flowing water? Badger thought they would. He died a few months after he announced his idea, but the idea itself has produced encouraging fruit. A pilot plant at Harbor Island, North Carolina, had by 1960 been desalting sea water by Badger's suggested method at the rate of 1200 gallons a day for many months, and the scaling problem "appeared to have been licked almost 100 per cent," according to Department of the Interior officials. In May 1960 the federal government let contracts for construction of a conversion plant which, using the Badger method, would produce a million gallons of fresh water daily out of the Gulf of Mexico at Freeport, Texas.

Even at a cost of $1 per 1000 gallons, fresh water from the sea is economically competitive with water from naturally fresh sources in several American localities. Key West, Florida, for example, must depend upon water pumped through a 90-mile pipeline from the Florida mainland at a cost of $1.05 per 1000 gallons. Until 1959 citizens of the small town (6021 people) of Coalinga in California's San Joaquin Valley were paying between $7.50 and $9.35 per 1000 gallons of drinking water trucked in from sources forty miles away—a fact which made it economically feasible for Coalinga to become the first American community whose drinking water came through a salt-water conversion plant. Placed in operation in 1959, the plant desalts local supplies of brackish water at the rate of 28,000 gallons daily and at a cost of $1.45 per 1000 gallons. It uses a membrane process. Presumably the Badger process, even at its present stage of imperfect development, could reduce by about one third the 1960 cost of Coalinga's water.

Of the other salt-water conversion processes, some of which involve freezing rather than boiling the water, several, still in the laboratory stage, are said to give promise of lowering the cost of conversion below 50 cents per 1000 gallons. If the promise is kept—if fresh water is ultimately obtained from the sea at no greater cost than that involved in obtaining it from naturally fresh sources—the consequences may well be more stupendous in terms of human life than those which have come thus far from the harnessing of nuclear energy, or are likely to come in the near future.

We've been talking about water shortages. There are also problems of localized and temporary water excesses—problems, in other words, of flood prevention and flood control. These are by no means contradictions of the over-all problem of lowered and lowering water tables. On the contrary, the latter problem is in considerable part a consequence of the same human operations that increase the number and severity of floods.

In a habitable but as yet uncivilized landscape, the soil is covered by living vegetation and by a blanket of dead vegetation, or humus. The leaves of trees and shrubs and grass break the force of falling rain, shattering large drops into smaller ones, which fall as a gentle spray upon the humus-blanketed earth. The humus acts as a sponge, soaking up the rain and sending it gently down among soil particles held together by humus and by the roots of living plants. The water is held where it falls until used by plants or until, through seepage, it becomes part of that continuous network of water (the water table) which spreads at various depths around the world. But when man marches upon the landscape, his ruthless will armed with ax and fire and plow, he turns back the clock toward that primitive time when all the earth's skin lay bare beneath the lash of rain. Stripped of their protective cover, great areas of sloping land can no longer soak up the falling water or hold their soil against it as it runs down into swelling streams and rivers and clogs their channels with erosion debris. Floodwaters thick with mud, clotted with trees and the ruins of man's constructions, spread across the valley.

And so, in our concern with water problems, we are brought at last to the river and to a realization that our problems of flood prevention and control, though they focus on the river, are by no means confined to it. Nor can they be truly solved in isolation from other problems also focused on the river but not limited to it. You recall that in our introduction we quoted Bernard Frank's statement that the whole story of man's growth might be written in terms of "his epic concerns with water." Well, the story goes on—and the essence of it can still be told in the terms Frank suggests. Most dramatically and in most accurate metaphor it can be told in terms of flowing water. The river, as man strives toward the best use of it, mirrors virtually every problem of ethics, politics, economics, technology.

Consider, for instance, the multiple aspects of a river and the disasters which derive from a failure to realize clearly that they are aspects—aspects of a single flowing reality—and not separate, static entities. A river, looked at from different points of view, is many functional things. It is an artery of commerce; a stream of raw power, capable of being converted into electricity; a flood menace which must be guarded against; an opportunity to transform parched lands into gardens; a source of drinking water; and a sewer. Each of these functions presents the river to our minds as a problem. It is a problem of creating or maintaining a navigable channel, a problem of hydro-electric-power development, a problem of flood control, a problem of irrigation, a problem of safe municipal water supply, a problem of pollution abatement. And all these problems, since they deal with aspects of a continuously flowing substance, interpenetrate and merge with one another. Each must be dealt with in terms of the others and, more importantly, in terms of the *whole* of which all are arbitrary abstractions. Moreover, the concept of this "whole" becomes ever deeper and wider as you proceed further and further toward final solutions.

If you are to maintain a navigable channel in the lower reaches of a river like the Missouri, say, you must use water wanted upstream for irrigation purposes. If you build downstream dams on such a river for the sole purpose of controlling floods, you cannot use these same dams efficiently for hydroelectric development, and vice versa. If you dump raw sewage into a river you may "solve" a local sewage-disposal problem, but you create a public-health menace downstream and destroy the river as a recreational area. Obviously, every big project you impose upon a river should have a multiple purpose; it should be designed to satisfy *in balance* a multiplicity of originally competing interests; and if it is to be ultimately satisfactory, the balance must be realized in terms of the river's essential nature.

But what is this essential nature? We say that the river is a flowing body of water defined by its source and mouth, by its flat surface facing the sky, and by the earthly bed and banks over which and between which it flows. These, however, are by no means the sharply delimiting boundaries of rivers which, at a casual glance, they seem to be. Look at these boundaries very closely and you see them as a watery blur wherein it is impossible to mark precisely the lines or points at which the river's flowing substance is distinguishable from the water which spreads around it. The river, you will see, is substantially continuous with the landscape it drains; it is fed by underground springs and seepages as well as by surface runoff; and even its surface tension is modified by evaporation as the wind and sun strike its surface, and its turbulence varies with the character of its bed. Ultimately satisfactory river planning therefore involves or implies consideration of whole watersheds.

CONCLUSION

We have come to the end of our essay. Is there significance in the fact that we end with the river?

We began, you recall, with a reference to Thales of Miletus, who believed, some 2500 years ago, that water is the universal substance of which all things are made. The metaphor he suggested was an infinite and eternal ocean of Being, a perfectly still water which only *seemed* to have motion. All its superficial agitations—its waves, its streams, its eddies—were a false appearance. Soon there were whole schools of Greek philosophers who could accept Thales's imagery as an essentially accurate view. Some of them spoke of an ocean of air rather than an ocean of water, others had other conceptions of the ultimate stuff, but all agreed that only Being (Permanence) is real. Becoming (Change) they proclaimed to be an illusion of the senses.

While Thales lived, there was born a Greek philosopher who took a very different view. Heraclitus of Ephesus proclaimed all Permanence to be illusion and only Change to be real. He was called "the Obscure" because of his love of paradox as he asserted, in a dozen different ways, that all Being is Becoming, all reality a flowing stream. Fire, said he, is the primordial element out of which everything comes and of which all is made. "This world . . . was ever, is now, and ever shall be an ever living Fire, with measures kindling and measures going out," he wrote, indicating his view of flame as a perpetual flux not unlike the river of which he spoke in one of the most famous of his aphorisms: "You cannot step twice into the same river, for fresh waters are ever flowing in upon you."

Now this essay of ours has, in one sense, moved from Thales toward Heraclitus as it developed. In our early chapters we dealt with water as a static substance, subject therefore to analysis. We spoke of its remarkable properties and made a brief historical survey of the discovery of water, meaning the exploration of what water *is* as a physical substance and as a manifestation of natural laws. We continued to deal with it as a static substance even when analysis had broken it down into the atoms of Democritus and John Dalton. The hard, massy, eternal atoms of oxygen and hydrogen constituting water were part of a substratum of Permanence supporting all the phenomena of Change. But when we attempted to "explain" water's unusual properties in the light of modern physics, we had to abandon this concept of the permanent or static altogether. We were driven to conclude that all is indeed a perpetual flux, and even a fiery flux as Heraclitus had proclaimed. Atoms proved to be whirls of motion, systems of electricity whose constituents were units of energy which may be viewed sometimes as particles, sometimes as waves. The universe, it appears, is fluid—a vast and ceaseless stream of Space-Time in which every thing is an event and all events are organically connected.

Hence the propriety of our ending with the river. We have tried to write our essay on water in terms of general science; we have written much of general science in terms of water, and our conclusion is that the natural world, as the scientist probes ever more deeply into it, reveals itself as a flowing reality analogous to a river. Like a river, it is paradoxical in that it is continually ceasing to be what it is and becoming what it is not while yet remaining what it always was. A principle of uncertainty seems to lie at its very heart.

One consequence is that it is now increasingly difficult to define science meaningfully in terms of the compartments set up at a more primitive stage of scientific development—the compartments of biology, geology, inorganic chemistry, organic chemistry, physics, and so on. Such precise compartmentalization was possible only when scientific investigation was concerned with the relatively superficial and static aspects of the natural world. In our time the distance that formerly separated the various branches of science has been annihilated. These branches have revealed themselves as extensions, like the branches of a tree, from a central trunk whose name is nuclear physics. And physics grows increasingly metaphysical in the literal meaning of this word (going beyond the physical into the realm of abstract idea) as it plunges ever more deeply into the stream of Space-Time.

INDEX

120674

SCIENCE STUDY SERIES